P135 Satan's Lies

*This book is a collection of stand-alone discussion guides designed for individual and family learning, couple counseling, and class group study

Table of Contents

Choosing a Real Man (A Spiritual Man)

1. Choose one who gets excited about the sermon when the preacher was less than exciting.
2. Choose one who knows the "unimportant people" in the eyes of the world.
3. Choose one who sits down in the cafeteria by the loners and the lonely instead of by the "in" group.
4. Choose one who can handle his temper when he is driving late, and a little old lady is driving 35 mph in front of him.
5. Choose one who joyfully participates in chapel instead of one who resents having to be there.
6. Choose one who can choose to be content when things aren't going well(One whose emotions are under the rule of his will).
7. Choose one who looks deeper than the outward physical appearance of people.
8. Choose one who is confident enough of his masculinity that he has no need to prove himself with clothes, trucks, physical feats (Those who are constantly trying to prove they are a man must have some personal doubts)
9. Choose someone bold in sharing their faith both in public and in private.
10. Choose someone who loves God more than they will ever love you (which means they will be able to love you more deeply because of Christ's love)
11. Choose someone who never blames the pitcher, the umpire, or the teacher for something that <u>might</u> be their own fault.

Choosing a Real Woman (A Spiritual Woman)

1. Pick someone whose inner beauty far exceeds her Beautiful outward appearance.
2. Choose someone who puts God first in the way they dress His Temple.
3. Choose someone who loves God more than they could ever love you.
4. Choose someone who has spiritual and charming qualities that will survive when her youthful beauty has gone.
5. Choose someone that knows how to love people who don't deserve it , and when they don't feel like it.
6. Choose someone who can enjoy life with, or without material possessions and a comfortable lifestyle.
7. Choose someone who loves you as you are, not for what they hope you will become.
8. Choose someone who will still love you when you get old, wrinked, fat and grouchy. (Do not choose someone who has chosen you based primarily on your looks, or on romantic feelings)
9. Choose a girl who hugs nobodies, and is willing to associate with people of lower reputation.
10. Choose someone who makes you laugh, and someone you can cry with and pray with.
11. Choose someone who will encourage you to grow in your relationship to Christ before you grow in your relationship with them.

Deep Discussions With Outstanding Spiritual Singles

<u>Instructions:</u>
Adjust or skip questions that are too uncomfortable or personal.
Both should share answers to the following:

1. Rate in order of importance to you the following life goals:___ personal
    comfort, ___a feeling of accomplishment, ___a successful family, ___spiritual growth,
    ___having fun in life, ___good health, ___safety and security, ___knowing you are
    loved, ___success and esteem in the eyes of friends,
    ___ being able to own some of the nice things in life.
    How would your parents have rated their life goals?
    (Discuss how differences in your parent's life goals created difficulty)

2. One thing I hope to do differently than my parents is...

3. I think churches would fulfill God's purpose better if...

4. One of the ways that the Devil has tried to destroy me is:
5. I sometimes wonder if God wants me to stop following my personal goals
    and...
6. One thing I wish I had done more in my life is...
7. I am really sorry that I...
8. Some hurts that I received in the past or from my family that don't usually share are...
9. One fear I have about my future is...
10. One lie I have believed about myself (from past hurts) is...
11. On a scale of 1-10 (1 is lowest, 10 is highest) my present relationship with God is...
12. If I move my relationship one notch higher I would need to...
13. One question I have about God, the Bible, or Spiritual things is:
14. One thing that I wish that my parents had done differently with me is...
15. If my family was asked what things I need to do to improve myself they would
    probably say:
16. I may have buried it inside, but It hurt me when...
17. I don't feel loved and appreciated as much if my family doesn't ...
18. One quality I wish I had more of is...
19. God loves me/doesn't like me much because...
20. I sometimes don't feel forgiven by God because...
21. One thing I really want to do, but have doubts about is...
22. The lost person whom I most long to be saved is _____because:
23. I sometimes feel sad/frustrated inside when...
24. I need people to empty out all of your past hurts and frustrations toward me so that we
    an....
25. I think that Satan wants us to hold all the little and big hurts/frustrations inside
    instead of sharing them because...
26. Some things I need others to pray about for me are...
27. Some things I regret from my past are...
28. Some ways I need other people to encourage me spiritually are...

Dr. Joe Brumfield

10. Describe what a perfect spouse would act like, do, etc.:

11. On a scale of 1-10 (1 is lowest, 10 is highest) rate your present relationship with God.

12. What would you have to do to move it up a notch?

13. One question I have about God, the Bible, or Spiritual things is:

14. One thing that I wish my parents had done differently with me is...

15. If my family was asked what things I need to do to improve myself they would probably say:

16. One of my talents is...

17. My favorite Bible hero is_____ because...

18. One quality I wish I had more of is...

19. God loves me because...

20. I sometimes don't feel forgiven by God because...

21. One thing I really want to do, but have doubts about is...

22. The lost person whom I most long to be saved is_____because:

23. I sometimes feel hurt inside when...

24. Regardless of how much money I make, I think the standard of living God wants me to live at is...

25. God has smiled on me in a special way by...

26. One way I wish my parents had been more strict on me is...

RECIPE FOR A MARRIAGE FAILURE
MARRY SOMEONE WHO:

1. Was rarely or never told "no!" as a child

2. Wants to live with you before marriage

3. Often fights and bickers---and must win!!

4. Will not let you grow as a person

5. Does not know how to communicate their feelings

6. Has not been trained to resolve problems

7. Does not have the same life goals as you
   (Different religion)

8. Does not want children, if you do--or vice-versa

9. Who cannot live without you. (They think they will
   finally be a whole person when they marry you)

10. Is very selfish, and thinks only of their own needs

11. Has unfinished emotional business with their parents
    that they refuse to deal with

12. Has a lack of personal self-discipline in matters of
    money, food, sex, etc.   Dr. Joe Brumfield, April 23, 1999

Part 2 TO HAVE A MARRIAGE FAILURE, MARRY SOMEONE WHO:

13. doesn't love the Lord more than you. (You may inadvertently be their idol to replace God)

14. Has a career that is more important to them than a marriage relationship

15. Has parents and friends who are all against the marriage

16. Believes that if it doesn't work, "we can always divorce"

17. Discourages your spiritual growth: prayer life, Bible study, Church attendance, relationship with God

18. Says "if you love me, you will sleep with me before we get married!" (They love themselves--not you!!)

19. Has parents who always took responsibility for the child's mistakes, and did not let them experience their own consequences

20. Has only stopped their bad habits since dating you: (alcohol, pornography, bad language, critical speech...)

21. Has only started their good habits since dating you: (Church attendance, Bible Study, positive speech, sharing feelings, resolving conflicts...)

Dr. Joe Brumfield, April 23, 1999

Uncovering Emotional Baggage

1. One way that I felt unaccepted by my parents was...

2. Sometimes my parents picked at me about...

3. Describe two qualities that a perfect spouse should have:

4. One thing that I really want to do...but I have doubts about is

5. One way I wish my parents had been stricter on me is...

6. One fear I have about my future is....

7. I think It might be hard to live with a spouse who...

8. One thing that someone did that made me feel "listened to" was...

9. One way the Devil has tried to destroy me is...

10. I sometimes wonder if God wants me to stop following my personal goals and...

11. One quality I wish I had more of is...

12. I sometimes don't feel forgiven by God because... One thing that might help me with this is...

13. One thing I wish my mom had said to me more was...

14. One way I fear that I'll be like my mom/dad is...

15. I sometimes feel like my parents would have loved me more if...

16. It was hard on me when my parents...

17. I wish people would ...

18. I'm sometimes afraid that people might think...

19. One reason people don't understand me is...

20. One thing my parents did that I will try to avoid is...

21. One trait that mother had that I will avoid is...

22. One trait that my dad had that I will avoid is...

23. It made me feel loved when my dad...

24. I long for people to consider me and think...

25. Sometimes I don't feel forgiven because...

Discussion With Teens About Dating

- What common mistakes do people make in High School Dating? (What mistakes did you make)
- Why do some people seem to be so desperate to be in a relationship?
- Why can't some girls/guys see how blind they are?
- Why do some girls only want to date a "jock" or someone popular?
- Why are some girls so "easy/touchy/needy?"
- Are people who are "fun" now—"fun" if you marry them?
- Why do some people not care about messing up their future?
- How will we know when we are mature enough to make wise choices about relationships?
- What are the advantages and disadvantages of dating now/later/ever?
- What early actions in relationships/dating could have helped solve common relationship problems that you see in therapy
- How do you "undo" mistakes that you have made?
- Just because a dating couple shares hugging and kissing doesn't mean they will go further---right?
- Are the people that you date going to be (later in life) what they seem to be now (happy, fun, romantic, flirty, exciting)
- When does dating make God jealous?
- Why do some married people act like they see things about dating that we don't see?
- Why does a person need to be emotionally whole before dating?
- Why do relationships make us feel apathetic about other things?
- Why do some feel like a man only if they are dating a cute girl?
- What makes you think that sexual activity now will damage my
- marriage some day?   (At least we didn't "do it")
- What kind of a girl does God want for me?
- What should I look for in a girl now that would predict that she would be a fun, exciting, spiritual, ravishing wife later?
- What are the benefits to spending lots of time with girls (being friends) without having an "exclusive relationship"
- How can you build intimacy in all areas w/o messing up?
- What activities would you recommend to build a great relationship?
- Which activities seem safe but are dangerous?

Dating: Exercise of Pretending

1. Dating is designed to produce fun, and to impress people with looks, gifts, and entertaining activities

2. Dating is not designed to examine people as possible future spouses or to assess future growth/potential.

3. Dating is likely to encourage lust, and therefore block an honest attempt to build long term relationships

4. Many believe that if they have sexual feelings for each other, they must be in love, and should therefore consider marriage.

5. Physical Intimacy of any kind often pressures dating couples toward a decision about marriage before they are ready. They either break up, or they get married and have serious problems because of their immaturity or lack of preparation.

6. People in "exclusive" dating relationships often let on other friendships and relationships. The dating actually damages social growth and friendships. Many people miss many of the wonderful experiences of college merely because they were so busy "dating."

Dating: Exercise in Pretending Continued

7. Many couples lose so much time and energy dating, that they make poor grades, and are less well prepared for their career. They actually damage their future marriage by poor early preparation for life.

8. Dating creates a "fake" atmosphere of fun, beauty, romance, entertainment, and relationship. People actually "trick" themselves into lifetime Miserable marriages because they get their cues from this fake environment, and make judgements about how life will be in the future. Many, possible even "most" people who are "good" at dating, are very "poor" at a lifetime "marriage."

   ***<u>Dating may actually be counterproductive</u> at finding/ producing what it claims to produce: a successful lifetime marriage, and a wonderful compatible mate.!!

Dating Dangers

1. Dating often arouses sexual desires that cannot be righteously satisfied
   a. Don't rev the engine when you have no good place to go!
   b. Will kissing make me desperate for more?
2. Dating causes chemical changes in the brain that make it nearly impossible to view the other person honestly and critically.
   a. Quiet people talk when dating.
   b. Depressed people may seem happy—a false picture
3. Dating teaches people how to have fun with each other but it does not give a picture of what marriage would be like together.
   a. Dating centers on having fun together
   b. Marriage centers on working out life together
4. Hugging and Kissing force people toward decisions that they are not ready to make.
5. Dating builds "intimacy" partners rather than friends.
6. Dating usually cripples growth in all other areas of life. You don't study to prepare for your career.
7. Dating damages other important relationships
8. Dating couples are fooled into thinking they are in love when they are only in "hormonal" love.
9. Many people miss the Harding experience and other life preparation.
10. Dating stops some people from the best preparation they could have for marriage!

Dr Joe Brumfield

Every Commonality Improves the Chances of a Good Marriage

1. Social Background
2. Economic Background
3. Religious Beliefs and Church Attendance
4. Desired Standard of Living
5. Child Rearing Practices
6. Life Goals
7. Use of Credit
8. Savings Practices
9. Political Affiliation
10. Desire for Social Activities
11. Hobbies
12. Music Style Preference
13. Movie Style Preference
14. Vacation Style
15. Family Background
16. Healthy Relationship with Parents
17. Desire for Romance in Marriage
18. Desire for Sex in Marriage
19. Family Healthy Communication Styles
20. Positive ability to Solve Problems
21. Career compatibility
22. Number of Children Desired
23. Belief about Husband/Wife Roles
24. Amount of Communication Desired
25. Friends shared in Common

**Differences may seem to attract people towards each other, but every area where people are similar increases the chances that they will get along well together for the long haul.

Dr. Joe Brumfield, Jan.4, 2000

Essential Discussion List for Serious Couples

Before You Decide To Marry Anyone--You Should Discuss and Make Decisions about the Following:

SPIRITUAL VALUES

-How important are spiritual matters to you now, and how important do you think they will be in the future? What are you committed to? What questions do you have about God, the church, and salvation? If you died today, would you go to heaven? What are your plans to keep your spiritual life growing? What are your parents' spiritual values? How were spiritual values taught in your home growing up?
What do you plan to do the same or differently? Do you love God? How much? Why? Are you led by the Spirit? Describe some of your efforts to share the good news with others? What is the most important goal in your life? Where are you now in your spiritual life?

COMMUNICATION

Describe the communication styles of your parents? Do they work things out as they happen, or store things up until they explode?
How do your parents share feelings in the home? Does your family regularly share their deep feelings with each other? Do you feel comfortable sharing your feelings, hurts, joys, sadness with your mom? Dad? Siblings? How good are your parents at really listening to each other? The children? Yourself? How do you check to see if what you heard is what they meant?

FAMILY PERSONALITY

Describe your family in great detail. How do they interact? Are they happy, sad, silly, serious, playful, etc. How do they treat each other? Are they distant from each other, or are they really close? Do they spend a lot of time together? How much? How much time do they spend together not counting mealtime, or TV time? Describe the personality of each family member, and then tell how you relate to them. Describe the ways you hope your spouse will be like your parent(s) and the ways you hope they'll be different.

ROLES FOR PARENTING, MARRIAGE, MONEY, WORK, HOUSEHOLD CHORES

In your present _and_ future family describe the following: who disciplines the kids and how, who feeds the baby? Changes diapers? Washes clothes? Washes dishes? Manages the checkbook? Carries the money? Decides what to spend? Decides how much to save? Who mows the grass? Services the car? Cleans the toilet? Vacuums the floor? (Make sure to hear plans for their future family)

PERSONAL PREFERENCES FOR ENTERTAINMENT, CLOTHES, POLITICS, CARS, LIFESTYLES, ETC.

What is your favorite actor? Movie? Music style? Vacation? Exercise? House style? City or country? Automobile?, color?, political party? On a scale of 1 to 10, how important are your preferences in each of the previous categories? Describe your least favorite of each of the previous categories. Who are some of your favorite musical performers? What music styles do you like the most? Dislike the most? Name the music/artists that you listen to the most.

PROBLEM SOLVING SKILLS & METHODS: PARENTS, SIBLINGS, FRIENDS

How do you solve problems and disagreements when they come up? How is this done by parents siblings and friends?
What may frustrate other people about how you deal with problems? How do you wish you would change? How do you want to handle disagreements differently than your parents?

POLITICAL & PHILOSOPHICAL VIEWS

Which political parties or views do you support? How strongly? How do you feel about people who support opposing parties? Describe your views about government, citizen involvement, current laws, etc. What kind of lifestyle do you think will please God? If you make 100,000 dollars per year, how nice a lifestyle do you plan to have? How much do you think one should be involved in political activities? Rallys? Financial contributions? Protests? Pro life? Abortion views? Foreign policy views? How flexible are you? What area or quality is your future spouse most likely to wish you would change?

Essential Discussion List for Serious Couples Continued

CHILD REARING BELIEFS AND STYLES

How many children do you hope to have some day? How do you think children should be raised? Disciplined? Who should do it? Do you believe in spanking? Describe how you think it should be done? Describe what your parents did. How do you hope to do it differently? How many things should children be given? Chores? Allowances? What kind of spiritual training do you plan to give your children? Describe in great detail, how you might carry this out. When will you allow your kids to date? Boys? Girls? What will be the requirements of going on dates? At what age do you think they should single date? Car date? What activities are proper and when? Will you buy your kids a car if you can? What social activities and school activities will you encourage your kids to be in? Which will you discourage? Which will you absolutely not allow? What values do you want to pass on to your children? What do you want to differently in child rearing than your parents did?

FEARS ABOUT MARRIAGE

How do you think the devil might try to destroy your future marriage? What problems have you seen in the marriages of others that you will try to avoid? Why do you think so many marriages fail today? What steps do you think couples should take to guard their marriages from failure? What attitudes do you think hurt marriage the most? When do you think people should get married? Divorced? What is an acceptable reason for divorce? Abuse? How much romance should be in marriage? Who should be in charge? Should both have an equal say in decisions? Who is the head of the house? What does this mean? What does submission mean? Who should submit to whom? How? How often should married partners share physical intimacy? When should physical intimacy be avoided?

PARENT PROBLEMS TO AVOID and MODELS TO KEEP

What things about your parents' marriage do you plan to imitate? What things will you avoid? How did they deal with conflict How involved do you want to be with your parents after marriage? Who should a couple visit on holidays? What if families can't be given equal time? Will you still follow your parent's rules? Will they have a key to your house? How involved do you want them to be in your life after you're married?

TIME USE

What activities are a waste of time? How much time should a husband and wife spend with each other? Talking time? Vacation time? Television time? Work time? Evangelism time? Time with kids? Music listening time? Time at work? Time doing office work at home? Time in social activities like little league, and sports practices? Time with Hobbies? Is it OK if husband watches TV while wife cleans house if both work?

FINANCES: SAVING, SPENDING, CONTROL, AND LIFESTYLES

How much should be saved? Given to God? Does your family follow a budget? How do they manage their finances? What lifestyle do you think will please God? Will you spend all you make to increase your house, car, possessions? What are your views on credit? What would you do if there isn't enough money left at the end of the month? Under what circumstances will your spouse not work? How long will one spouse stay home with the kids? How much are you willing to sacrifice for your kids: clothes? School? Friend choice? Christian Education? Health? Toys? Entertainment? Describe how you think a married couple should handle money.

PERSONAL LIFE PRIORITIES AND GOALS

 Rate the following in importance to you:

- **Safety and security in life**
- **Being highly esteemed and socially acceptable**
- **Having some fun and enjoyment in life**
- **Saving for old age**
- **Health**
- **Major life achievement and career**
- **Having some nice things in life**
- **Spiritual accomplishment**
- **Family Closeness**

MY WEDDING VOWS TO YOU

-I promise to show love and patience even when you don't deserve it.

-I promise to be your best friend.

-I promise to treat you with kindness even if I don't feel like it.

-I'll seek your best interest because of my commitment to God.

-I will always honor you, and I'll never bring up old issues that we have already dealt with.

-I will never compare you in my mind with other people.. I won't even shop around in my mind.

-I will be patient with you even when you have P.M.S. or a hard day.

-I promise to forgive you based on God's forgiveness of me when I didn't deserve it --not based on what you deserve.

-I'll try to understand your feelings & I will honestly share my feelings.

-I will never go to bed angry at you. I will stay up and talk it out.

-I won't hold secret things against you. I will be honest about my hurts and frustrations.

-I'll turn the T.V. off, put the newspaper down, or sit up in bed when you want me to listen.

-I will try to make every word I say to you one of encouragement and upbuilding for your needs.

-I will meet your physical, emotional, and spiritual needs....

-I will love you forever.

We make these vows in the sight of God

_____ and _____
               Vow maker   Vow maker

Witness: _____

Date:_____

Witness: _____

Date:_____

Joe Brumfield

16a

Marry Someone Who Is Not Afraid To Apologize

Date and marry someone who often says, " that was my fault" "I messed up!" "My Bad"---avoid dating people who blame someone or something-----avoid them like the plague!

"Real Men are quick to accept full responsibility for their mistakes----weak men make excuses, and attempt to wiggle out of blame"

Chapman and Thomas give five important steps in their <u>Five Languages of Apology</u>:
1. Admit your mistake
2. Say you are sorry
3. Take responsibility
4. Repenting—share your desire to never repeat the offense--- "I don't want to ever do this again---could you help me think of ways to avoid this problem?"
5. Ask for forgiveness: Be very clear about it!!

Help your kids build a great marriage 20 years in advance! Teach your kids to say they are sorry. Teach your kids (and yourself) not to give "half" apologies by saying, "I'm sorry but…"   Adding the "but" is often your unconscious attempt to avoid your responsibility!   Blaming others damages relationships!!   Teach them to say, "I spilled the milk" Not , "the milk spilled"

Teach your kids, "If you break the rules---there will be consequences.
   Do not rescue your kids from the consequences of their poor choices.   Some of the most damaged children had "overly helpful" parents who always did the apologizing for their kids. These parents went to school to "blame the teacher" and "excuse the bad behavior" of their child. Do not marry one of these kids!   They have been trained to be "blamers.!

The "I Feel" Deal
By Dr. Joe Brumfield

After the Honeymoon comes the real Marriage where two sinners (forgiven or not) begin real life with each other. A marriage killing decision looms near:
Most married couples decide to stop sharing hurt feelings with each other because sharing them leads to painful battles.

Couples throw verbal arrows back and forth and escalation (emotional slaughter) begins. Louder words and cutting remarks lead to fighting, sexual refusal, cold wars, etc. The verbal battles cause so much pain that the couple begins holding in frustrations. They avoid the pain of battle by choosing a hurt that is only less at the beginning: keeping hurt feelings inside oneself. As hurts build up, marital satisfaction goes down. People become a smoldering volcano—ready to explode!

The "I Feel" Deal is an agreement to share every hurt feeling and frustration with the spouse. The spouse in turn agrees to say "Thank you for sharing" and then to say nothing in return for at least one hour. (The desire to "hit back" with words subsides)

A person can agree to hear hurt feelings knowing that their spouse is giving information that they ordinarily might withhold—rather than sharing to start a fight. These feelings are being shared to give information that is needed for understanding.

To begin sharing say, "I feel deal?" Spouse responds, "Please share!"
Then share one of the following feelings knowing that your spouse cares enough to hear in a loving manner:
Honey (always start with a term of endearment)
I feel hurt when...
I feel put down when...
In situation ( ) when you ( ), I feel ( )
I feel frustrated when...
I feel hurt when...
I don't feel loved when...
I feel less appreciated when...

Premarital: About Sex and the Honeymoon
Dr. Joe Brumfield

1. you are different: you will have to coach each other: tell each other what you want, what you need, what you like, and what turns you on and off
2. Explain that there is no switch---it is a process taking time to finally feel safe in "letting yourself go to enjoy sex...it is good, pure, beautiful and wonderful"
3. It is extremely vulnerable to be out of control in front of someone else
4. bodies belong to each other: you are there for their sexual pleasure---
5. Mutual orgasm is not a requirement
6. Meeting their needs can be your fulfillment
7. Letting someone meet your needs is important
8. Will you promise to let me know what you need and want even if you are not comfortable at the time telling me!
9. Part of his enjoyment is you "Wanting Him, and feeling like he caused you to share the thrill"
10. A husband would rather shovel snow in sub zero weather than know that his wife disrespects him (Go ahead if you gotta, but hurry up and get it done)
11. No expectations: No orgasms required
12. Lots of laughter and lubrication
13. Birth control--- at least 3 months ---
14. Sexual past: risk of Aids
15. Comparison kills contentment
16. Discussion of "Not traditional" sexual contact
    a. When one is not "interested" In sex: Negotiation: Choosing to be interested:
17. Sex is wrong when: it makes her feel "dirty" or "bad" or "unsafe" or "used" when it "hurts"   ....flashbacks.. when angry...
18. Sex at night begins in the morning

Top Needs of Husbands and Wives

Wise people use their time and energy to meet the most important needs of
their spouse. Unwise people use up their time and energy meeting
less important needs. Have your Spouse rate their important needs so
you can give first priority to the most important ones:

Husband Needs:	Wife Needs:
___honor and admiration	___Romance
___have sexual needs met	___more communication
___peace at home	___help with the kids
___mutual hobbies	___non-sexual touch
___quiet and gentle spirited wife	___spiritual leader husband
___wife satisfied with our income	___more rest to avoid fatigue
___respect from wife	___compliments
___a wife who keeps fit	___transparent feelings
___private time	___relief from time pressure
___happy attitude	___acceptance and forgiveness
___acceptance and forgiveness	___spiritual growth
___spiritual growth	___spontaneous show of caring

Dr. Joe Brumfield Jan. 4, 2000

Willard Harley, in his book, His Needs, Her Needs suggests that
the top needs of Husbands are:
1. Sexual fulfillment
2. Recreational Companionship
3. Physical Attractiveness
4. Domestic Tranquility
5. Admiration

Harley further suggests that the top needs of Wives are:
1. Affection
2. Conversation
3. Honesty and Openness
4. Financial Support
5. Family Support

The Secret To Relationships With Men In Your Life

1. You cannot have good relationships with your husband, your sons, your father, and all other men until you understand that their greatest need is to be respected and honored. They need this like they need food. Men are extremely fragile in the area of feeling dishonored or disrespected. They also feel the need to pretend that they are not.

2. Their greatest fear, frustration, and hurt is to be disrespected. Men are constantly sniffing the air to sense in every word, interaction, job…how much respect or disrespect is being shown or inferred. Every word, every voice tone, and every movement a woman makes is carefully measured by the men around them for respect or disrespect.

3. Every man moves toward the things and the relationships that give him more respect and value. This is the reason some men play golf, hunt, fish, stay at work, avoid going home, avoid going to church…etc.

4. Men increase every activity where they received even a scrap of value. If another man hears that I caught a big fish, and even hints "You're the man!! I will go fishing again. If my wife even hints by her voice tone that she disrespects me, I may avoid going home. Many wives don't realize that their conversation "drips with thinly disguised disrespect." Their talk is the exact reason that their husband doesn't want to "share his heart" with them. "Correcting your husband's work, ideas, driving, thoughts…is almost always viewed as disrespect.

5. Men will join any group, sport, or activity where they get a few scraps of value. They may be 75, but they will still go drink coffee regularly with other men who will give them value by laughing at their jokes, and listening to their stories. All men are desperate to find something that makes them believe they are "man enough." This is part of the reason men are in competition with all other men….every day. They long for someone to convince them that they are a WINNER and that they have finally reached the respect and admiration level of a "real man!"

Dr Joe Brumfield
Dec 2008

UNDERSTANDING WIVES' FEELINGS, EMOTIONS AND STRESSES

1. Having to be the sole caretaker of the children
   a. physical   b. emotional   c. spiritual
2. Lack of Romantic love in marriage
3. Longing for non-sexual touch
4. Desire for deep emotional sharing--without begging
5. No time for taking care of "my needs" too busy caring for husband and children
6. Not enough rest and relaxation.
7. Pressure and stress to "hurry"
8. Great expectations of husband
9. A day job, and "full time" housework
10. My husband takes me for granted
11. I'm expected to be a beauty queen, while given the duties of a slave
12. My husband does not "long to share" with me
13. "I feel pressure to Perform" in bed--I can't just be me
14. I have to be the spiritual leader in our home
15. I want to feel more secure, and not be constantly under financial stress
16. My husband shows his love in ways that don't speak to the ways that make me feel loved
17. My husband thinks I'm trying to manipulate or change him, when all I want is to help him reach his Full potential
18. My husband is not happy with life, and I feel helpless to assist him
19. We don't dream together anymore
20. I'm not growing spiritually and I need a friend

Why I Rarely Compliment My Husband

(Rationalizations from Wives)

1. He doesn't do it for me!
2. He already knows what I think.
3. He is a slob – there is nothing good to say about him.
4. I refuse to lie.
5. He might quit growing.
6. I don't know how to compliment him.
7. I didn't see it done when I was growing up.
8. I don't feel like it.

Why I Rarely Compliment My Wife

(Rationalizations from Husbands)

1. She doesn't make me feel loved.
2. She doesn't make me feel respected.
3. .....all of the same rationalizations from above!
4. "the sky is blue".......after all one rationalization is as good as another!

Joe Brumfield

18b

UNDERSTANDING THE NEEDS, FRUSTRATIONS AND FEARS OF HUSBANDS

1. He frequently doesn't like himself
2. Feeling of escaping youth
3. Sex requires too much work, romance, etc.
4. He wishes his wife would see him as her hero--he longs to feel like one
5. Longs for wife to "crave" physical intimacy
6. Desires lots of attention-but won't ask
7. Wants wife to be beautiful--and stay beautiful!
8. Enjoys having a home that is peaceful, and enjoyable
9. Wants home that is a refuge not a battlefield
10. Wants to be "babied" but not treated like a child
11. Craves time to relax without pressures
12. Likes "fun activities with wife--laughter not just bills"
13. Desires time by himself without guilt
14. Fears degeneration of his physical body
15. Wants honor and respect
16. Desires mutual interests and hobbies with wife
17. Would like wife to be a playmate as well as a working partner
18. Needs an Understanding of his sexual needs and desires sometimes feels guilty for having needs and desires
19. Needs excitement and challenges for the future
20. He longs for a happy and contented Spouse

Dr. Joe Brumfield/ 1997

Suggestions for Women Who Want To Help Make Their Man Feel Like a "Real Man"   Dr Joe Brumfield

Why is He or She so "touchy?"

Remember that people get angry over what your words made them feel, not the facts of your words. Your words touched an emotional wound from the past. Example : My Daddy wasn't there for me---I felt abandoned by my dad, so anything you say (awakens feelings and fears from the past) "makes me angry" or actually makes me desperately afraid inside.   That's why I can't take male criticism, and why I have to be in control of things: I'm trying to avoid a repeat of my childhood pain from feeling abandoned or unloved by my dad…

1. Treat them the way to be treated because it is right, not as a way to manipulate them into giving what you want. They will probably respond in kind, but, be careful not to foster "conditional love" I'll love you if….

2. Proverbs warns three times about the dangers of a wife who is nagging. Die to yourself!   Remember, your kids have their mental video cameras on 24/7.   When you nag, your husband hears several messages (based on his inner fears and doubts from the past) He may hear: "you are such a child, you will forget if I don't remind you" "You are not a real man, or you would read my mind," "I don't trust you to be responsible," You are not an adult"… "You are lazy, You are inadequate"…..   DON'T WASTE YOUR TIME TELLING YOURSELF THAT YOU DIDN'T SEND THESE MESSAGES.   HIS RECEIVING SENSORS ARE MORE INFLUENCED BY HIS PAST THAN BY YOU"   You are responsible for the messages he is receiving from you, not the ones you think you sent.   So is He!   Read Eph 4: 29 again! We are actually commanded to say only things that build people up according to their needs!

3. If you want your husband to do more, do the opposite of nagging.   Try honest BRAGGING!   Tell your friends, kids, and inlaws about the great things that your husband has done. I bet it gets back to him! EVERY HONESTLY COMPLIMENTED BEHAVIOR WILL LIKELY INCREASE!!   Follow that imperfect man around until you notice him do something right, and then…tell him how much you respect and admire him for it.

Suggestions for Women Who Want To Help Make Their Man Feel Like a "Real Man" Continued by Dr Joe Brumfield

4. Here is how to ask Him to do something, "Hey, you big, strong handsome man, is there any way you could get this jar of canned peaches opened? He will get it done if he has to use TNT!! All MEN MOVE IN THE DIRECTION OF THE ACTIVITIES, FRIENDS, AND COMMUNICATION THAT SAY, "YOU HAVE WHAT IT TAKES….YOU ARE ADEQUATE AND MORE…..YOU ARE A REAL MAN" Do not fake compliments! Flattery is deceitful. And Liars go to hell (it actually says that in the Bible: Revelation 21:8)

5. Fussing is Futile! If you "win a fight with your spouse, and convince them that they are, "Wrong, dumb, incompetent, mean, stupid, ugly, inadequate" …what did you win?? An emotionally bleeding and bruised spouse! Stomp your left foot with your right foot….prove that the left foot is wrong….What did you win? Your spouse is part of you! Ever hear of "one flesh?"

6. Notice the difference that encouragement makes: it seems like your spouse keeps track of all of your mistakes versus "that makes me so happy when you take out the trash" Love keeps no record of wrongs.

7. Everyone needs appreciation. Ignore their mistakes and praise their successes. Mistakes will decrease, and good behavior will increase!

8. The more you act positively about anything--the more they will do it.

9. How Can Wives communicate well?
   a. It is easy to get what you want if you do it correctly.
   b. Husbands are impressed by honesty, not emotional blackmail
   c. Make sincere short requests
   d. If you treat us like the expert—we husbands become that
   e. Asking with appreciation, approval, admiration--we will do almost anything
   f. Don't forget, a happy husband is better than a clean kitchen!

10. Be a female: don't get frumpy and grouchy: wearing sweats and get a defensive attitude. Instead, smell sweet, put on sexy outfits, and be nice!

12. Create a positive emotional atmosphere and he will want to come home.

13. Don't let yourself go—dress nice and look nice for him--not for work

14. Quit finding things to criticize him for. It will backfire! Even so called "constructive criticism" discourages and kills his motivation.

Real Men

What do they do when led by the Spirit:

1. Compliment their wife when everyone else is telling "wife"
   jokes
2. Pray with their family, and call them by name to God
3. Share their feelings instead of bury them
4. Ask for directions
5. Go shopping with their spouse when they don't want
   to--and they make themselves like it!
6. Turn off the TV when bad language comes on, even it it's
   their own favorite program
7. Say their sorry without being forced to, or being proven
   wrong
8. Are not afraid to play dolls with their little girl.
9. Joyfully carry out the trash in the middle of their favorite
   ball game if their wife asks them to
10. Put their wife before their children, their buddies,
    hunting, fishing, golf, etc.
11. Cry!
12. Clean the bathroom and hang up their clothes without
    being asked
13. Fight for family spiritual activity when the world puts
    heavy pressures to squeeze it out
14. Have a positive and cheerful disposition even when they
    are tired and discouraged
15. Volunteer to clean the toilet, and change the "dirty"
    diapers
16. Are not afraid to confess their sins and mistakes

Real men:

17. Give hugs and non-sexual touch to their wives with no ulterior motives.
18. Give regular sincere compliments and words of appreciation to their wives and children, even when they aren't getting any
19. Don't pass the buck and blame others for their mistakes in sports etc. "They don't say 'blind umpire', 'bad pitch', 'they cheated', etc
20. Hug
21. Don't use 'strong' language that 'weak' people seem to need.
22. Don't have to have macho trucks, tools, guns, clothes etc to prove their manhood. People who have doubts about their manhood are often trying to show it or prove it.
23. Good listeners- consider needs of others first
24. Sacrifice their own pleasures and desires for the good of their family
25. Confess Jesus in public without shame.
26. Let women cry without feeling uncomfortable
27. Can show feelings and show emotions.
28. Tell kids "I love you."
29. Admit when their wrong.
30. Don't gloat when they win
31. Discipline their children and train kids in righteousness
32. Are not threatened by the accomplishments of others
33. Lead family spiritually by actions
34. Put their families ahead of their jobs

Real Women:

(Led by the Spirit)

1. Put their husband's esteem before the kids, or before the housework
2. Work on their inner beauty as a priority above their external beauty
3. Have a quiet and gentle spirit even when the world calls them a "doormat"
4. Are their husbands number One cheerleader
5. Honor God with their physical body: eat right and exercise and try to stay healthy
6. Call their husband Lord, or Master, or the cultural equivalent today
7. Have the ability and the inclination to give respect and honor to their husband, even when he deserves little or none.
8. Give husband lots of physical intimacy without being asked--and makes herself enjoy it
9. Compliment their husband in public as well as in private
10. Make their husband feel good about himself
11. Are able to pump their own gas, and change their own tire, but somehow make their husband want to do it.
12. Have a great spiritual relationship with God, even when their husband does not lead spiritually
13. Encourage their husbands to want to be a spiritual leader
14. Always support the husband to the children

You Are Not A Real Man If You:

1. Retaliate

2. Prey on young women's low self-esteem

3. Have to win argument

4. Beat your wife or girlfriend to prove self

5. Have to fight or compete to feel valuable

6. Make fun of others to build yourself up

7. Don't listen

8. Get their identity from things- not GOD

9. Don't listen or talk- don't communicate

10. Have to have your own way

Joe Brumfield, Oct 8, 1999

23

Marriage Tune-up For Husbands

Find a warm romantic atmosphere, and ask your wife the following questions:

1. What can I do that will make you feel more "romanced?"
2. What can I do that will make you feel that I am sharing my deepest feelings with you?
3. What can I do so that all of the things I have done in the past to hurt you will be gone forever?
4. What can I change to make you feel better about my role in rearing our children?
5. What can I do that will make you feel that I am doing more than my share of the housework?
6. What can I do to make you feel less fatigue and time pressure?
7. What can I do to make you feel more spiritually encouraged?
8. What can I do to make you feel that I am being an effective spiritual leader for our family?
9. What can I do to make you feel more loved?
10. What can I do to make you feel more secure and satisfied regarding the future of our marriage?

Dr. Joe Brumfield
Harding University

Marital Tune-Up For Wives: Checking the Oil, and Changing the Spark Plugs in Your Marriage

Take your husband out for his favorite meal, then find a quiet romantic place and ask him the following serious questions:

1. "Honey, (always start with a term of endearment) what can I do to make you feel more admired and respected?"
2. What can I do to make you know how much I enjoy our love life together?
3. What can I do to make you feel that our home is an enjoyable, warm, and encouraging place for you?
4. What can I do to make you feel that I am satisfied and happy with the income that you bring home?
5. What can I do to make you know how much we all need you?
6. What can I do to make you feel better about our future life goals together?
7. What quality would you like me to improve on?
8. What quality would you like me to encourage you to build?
9. What could I do to make you feel more successful in the spiritual leadership of our home?
10. What recreational activities could we do together that would help you feel that we have lots of fun together?
11. What could I do that would make me more attractive to you?
12. What could I do to help you in your personal spiritual growth?

Dr. Joe Brumfield
Harding University

Satan's Outline For Adultery

1. Emotional and Sexual Needs not being met
2. Opportunity: chance meeting with beautiful woman, secretary, etc.
3. Eyes Meet...Casual friendship
4. Casual or business conversation/ no intent to sin
5. Compliments and kind words--emotional account building up
6. Accidental or purposeful hand touch
7. Romantic interest in the mind/Emotional betrayal of spouse
8. What If Scenarios reviewed
9. Mental rationalizations to reduce guilt for mental fantasy
10. Spiritual rationalizations to reduce cognitive dissonance
11. Longer business meetings and lunches
12. More time at the office and less at home/ Secrecy
13. Nervous excitement regarding risk and fulfillment
14. Sexual fantasy, and masturbation
15. Progression of touching....then a quick kiss..
16. Clear and Conscious planning of time together-no more pretending
17. More Physical boundaries broken- Selfish Pleasure
18. Sexual Intercourse/pleasure ****ADULTERY
19. Guilt/momentary repentant thoughts/ rationalize and repeat Sexual Sin/....less guilt...more rationalization....more sin...feeling it's too late to stop now...might as well continue...
20. Discovered! Caught!! Shame! Incredible Spouse pain!!! (more than losing a spouse to death) Children damaged !!
21. Loss of Reputation, Loss of Respect, Family tortured, shamed, betrayed, and now split apart in DIVORCE
22. Total Spiritual Failure!
23. Lifetime effects on Self, Spouse and Children
24. Judgement!

James 1:13-15 No one should say when they are tempted that God is tempting them, because God cannot be tempted by evil and he does not tempt anyone--but each person is tempted when they are dragged away and enticed by their own evil desire. Then after desire has conceived, it gives birth to sin--and when sin is full grown it gives birth to death."

Revised by Brumfield, Jan 2000

Most Common Reasons For Divorce
Root Reason: Blind Selfishness

1. Different life goals, philosophies and beliefs (Spiritual Goals versus Material Goals)
2. Failure to help spouse like himself or herself
3. Failure to meet Sexual and Emotional Needs
4. Decline of Prayer, Church Attendance and Bible Study
5. Deep rooted and blind focus on self and personal needs and desires
6. Poor communication skills/practice
7. Money Problems and Stresses
8. Alcohol or Drug problems
9. Inability to trust spouse
10. Constant Criticism and Negativity
11. Stifling growth of spouse because of personal insecurity
12. Financial and Time stress from rearing children
13. Too Busy: failed to take time to build the marriage
14. Divorce is easy and socially acceptable
15. Death of Loving non-sexual touch
16. Belief that spouse can meet all my needs and <u>make</u> me happy
17. Adultery
18. Lack of compliments, encouragement and appreciation
19. Pornography
20. Influence of negative role models: people, music, media
21. Emotional baggage/hurts from the past unresolved

Adapted with George Barna's list of 13 most common
Causes of Divorce

Dr. Joe Brumfield
Aug 2000

10 Commandments For Building A Fantastic Marriage

By Dr Joe Brumfield

1. Work on your personal relationship with God: nothing will improve your marriage more than this. Make sure God is far above family, job, or marriage. Don't try to make your spouse be your God who gives you purpose, value, and healing.

2. Read your Bible and Pray daily with Spouse. Never miss meeting with God's Family: this drops your divorce rate to less than one out of 1000.

3. Speak In your Spouse's love language instead of your own: become a student of their language. Ask them what you have done in the last week or month that made them "feel loved." Do more of this kind of thing.

4. Give 10 positive messages for every negative one: smiles, hugs, and tender voice tone count!

5. Admit when you are wrong and apologize : take responsibility for your "stuff." Empty this trash immediately! You will be healthier and happier if your own heart is at peace.

6. Romance your spouse in the way that speaks to them rather than in the way that speaks to you.

7. Put your spouse before your kids. This is the best gift you can give your kids!

8. Treat your spouse like you want to be treated: Become your spouses "Dream man or woman" If that means do the dishes, or help with the kids, or lose weight, or wear different clothes, or becoming a spiritual leader—do it!!

9. Share regular sex—never stop this except for agreed on times of prayer and/or fasting. Satan is waiting for you to stop regular intimacy because it gives him a huge opening into your heart and life.

10. Eliminate from your conversation anything that does not build your spouse up in things they need (Eph 4:29) Everything should be positive and encouraging. Make sure your body language and voice tone is positive as well

STRANGE THINGS SOME HUSBANDS LIKE
(A ridiculous list of what some husbands want even when they don't always deserve it)

1. Hand written love notes--not store ought cards or flowers
    --weekly, or twice a month is about right
2. Wife initiated intimacy (only 1 out of 4 times or so)
3. Beautiful smiles and hugs
4. Wife initiated kisses (half of the time)
5. Regular forgiveness for the many mistakes made by husband
6. Daily words of appreciation
7. Little or no constructive criticism
    ask the husband to critique himself, and then tell him how to what
    extent you agree. This is much less painful
8. Compliments for good things done--complimented
9. Verbal communication anytime wife is feeling resentful
    about kids, house, laundry, tired husband. Some husbands
    would rather know clearly rather than constantly guess.
10. Wife to ask for what she wants rather than be frustrated when
    husband doesn't do, or even know: kisses, foot rubs, help with
    dishes, more romance, weekly date.... how about a list just like
    this one from the wives??? Please, Please...
11. Wife to go to bed earlier and get more rest--understanding that this
    may be beyond her control with so many pressing late night duties
    ---but when one is dreaming--dream big
12. To be admired by wife as her hero--of course he would have to
    live up to it--perhaps a nearly impossible task
13. To sing songs together in the car
14. To read the Bible together more, and pray together more
    ----of course--what is stopping some husbands from getting most of this stuff--   the ball
    is in the husbands court
15. Maybe most of all--some husbands actually long to be the man of
    her dreams, and greatly dislike themselves when they fail to be

Common Fears of Men in Midlife Crisis

1. fear of growing old
2. fear not being attracted to ones' wife
3. fear that wife will not be attracted to husband
4. fear being trapped in an unfulfilling marriage
5. guilt over lust, failure, procrastination, and other sin
6. fear of having a heart attack, stroke, etc.
7. fear of looking unseemly and of being athletically unfit
8. fear of not being loved by spouse, kids, friends etc.
9. fear of losing the respect of spouse, children, etc.
10. fear of children failing spiritually, socially, or in dating/marriage
11. fear of being unsuccessful on the job
12. fear of failing to prepare financially for the future
13. fear of going to hell, or of displeasing God
14. fear of dying
15. fear of being unknown or disrespected socially
16. fear of not being able to compete
17. fear of people finding out personal faults, failures, and sins
18. fear of wasting ones' life
19. fear of losing sexual desire or performance ability
20. fear of not being able to pay off debts or of wasting money and resources
21. fear of not being a "real" Christian
22. fear of major loss: being in an accident, being sued, etc.
23. fear of kids being killed, abused, or emotionally damaged
24. fear of yielding to sinful temptations
25. fear of disappointing family & friends

Dr. Joe Brumfield 2002

Dr. Paul Meier suggests that anxiety is fear of the unknown. Fear of finding out the truth about our thoughts, motives and feelings—The Holy Spirit is pushing the truth up, and our depravity is pushing it back down. This constant battle causes great anxiety!!!!

Making Your Spouse Crazy About You Again

1. Trash the idea that your spouse can/must make you happy.
2. Avoid trying to meet most of your emotional & esteem needs through your spouse.
3. Work on getting your emotional needs met by God: feeling loved, valued, accepted, needed, wanted.

Words That Build Fulfilling Marriages

Ephesians 4:29 commands us to speak only things that build
others up. Couples who give each other five times more positive
messages than negative messages can be predicted to have a marriage
that will last a lifetime. Which of the following things do you need to say
more:

1. "I am so glad that I married you".
2. "If I had to choose all over again, I would choose you."
3. "I love you!" (You can't say this too much if it's sincere)
4. "I have been thanking God for you today!"
5. "I love the way you smile"
6. "I love coming home to you after a hard day at work"
7. " I was wrong!"
8. "I am sorry!"
9. "Please forgive me!"
10. "I need you."
11. "You always encourage me"
12. "You are such a good mother/father"
13. "I will always love you"
14. "I hope our children have a personality just like yours"
15. "God made a treasure when he made you!"
16. "I dream of growing old with you!"
17. "When I first met you, I could see that you were one of
    God's special creations!"
18. "I don't know what I would do without you!"
19. "Hugging you makes me feel warm inside."
20. "I'm always happy when you are around."

Joe Brumfield and Lindsey Brumfield 2-7-2000

Words That Destroy Your Marriage

"And be ye kind one to another, tenderhearted, forgiving one another, even as God for Christ's sake hath forgiven you." Ephesians 4:32

1. "You're just like your mother."
2. "You just don't think do you."
3. "You're just a baby."
4. "Is that the way you're going to wear your hair?"
5. "Why don't you drop dead?"
6. "I wish I'd never married you."
7. "I don't love you anymore"
8. "Hey thunder thighs"
9. "You don't excite me anymore."
10. "I could do just as well without you."
11. "You're so _____" (insert term of contempt like dumb,
    a. stupid, idiot, fickle, or any other Raca)
12. "You always _____" (insert any put-down) "you" is an attack word, and "always" doubles the insult.
13. "You never _____" (insert anything you have wished for them to do) "never" doubles the attack
14. "You embarrass me!"
15. "I feel trapped when I'm with you!"
16. "Women and children off the sidewalk" (joking about spouse's driving)
17. "You never could do anything right"
18. "I wish I'd married _____"(insert name of old flame)
19. "You're costing me an arm and a leg"
20. "You just don't think, do you?"
21. "You call that clean?"
22. "You just bought those flowers for me because they were half price!" (Motive doubting statements)
23. "You're probably thinking _____" (negative mind reading)
24. "Why don't you grow up?"
25. "It's all your fault!"

Dr. Joe Brumfield 2-08-2000

31h

Communication: What the Bible says about it:

1. Want a Great life? <u>1 Peter 3:10</u> For, "Whoever would love life and see good days must keep his tongue from evil and his lips from deceitful speech.

2. <u>Nothing good to say?</u> Eph 4:29 Speak only what is good for building others up according to their needs

3. Straight talk!! <u>Matthew 5:37</u> Simply let your 'Yes' be 'Yes,' and your 'No,' 'No'; anything beyond this comes from the evil one.)

4. Want to be condemned?<u>James 5:12</u> Above all, my brothers, do not swear—not by heaven or by earth or by anything else. Let your "Yes" be yes, and your "No," no, or you will be condemned.

5. Nice Juicy Kiss? <u>Proverbs 24:26</u> An honest answer is like a kiss on the lips

6. Stop a fight? <u>Proverbs 15:1</u> A gentle answer turns away wrath, but a harsh word stirs up anger.

7. How Nice? <u>Ephesians 4:32</u> Be kind and compassionate to one another, forgiving each other, just as in Christ God forgave you

8. <u>Prayer Killer?</u> 1 Pet 3:5-7 Treat wife with consideration and respect or your prayers will be hindered

9. <u>Talk Slow?</u> James 1:19 My dear brothers, take note of this: Everyone should be quick to listen, slow to speak and slow to become angry

10. Words show Character? <u>Luke 6:45</u> The good man brings good things out of the good stored up in his heart, and the evil man brings evil things out of the evil stored up in his heart. For out of the overflow of his heart his mouth speaks.!!

11. Judgment test? <u>Matthew 12:36-38</u> 36But I tell you that men will have to give account on the day of judgment for every careless word they have spoken. 37For by your words you will be acquitted, and by your words you will be condemned."

12. Nagging? Proverbs 19, 21, 25, 27, corner of the roof, constant dripping, live in the desert 5x quarrelsome wife in Proverbs 21:19 Better to live in a desert than with a quarrelsome and ill-tempered wife.

13. People Rule? Matt 7:12 Do unto others as you would have them do unto you.

How To Communicate Feelings of Frustration

Do not say it like this: You drive me insane!   I regret marrying you.   You are just like your mother!

A better way to share hurt and frustration is the * <u>One, Two, Three Method:</u>

"In situation <u>One</u>"

"When you do <u>Two</u>"

"I feel <u>Three</u>"

Example:

When we are visiting with our friends from Church, (ONE)

And you tell them about all of my mistakes and failures (TWO)

I feel betrayed and angry! (Three)

Example:

When we are sharing romantic feelings   (One)

And you make disrespectful comments about me, (Two)

I feel frustrated and lose romantic feelings. (Three)

Each communication should contain a WHEN, a WHAT, and a HOW it makes me FEEL.   Always use an "I feel" phrase when possible!

*Sometimes called the ABC method, the "Van Pelt" method, and other names.

Messages Your Family Needs To Hear And Believe

1. "I Love You!" "My love is not based on your performance in school, in sports, or in anything else!"
2. "It's all right that you messed up."
3. "I forgive you!"
4. "I'm so proud of you"
5. "I need you!"
6. "I'm thankful that God blessed my life by sending you to be a part of our family!"
7. "I appreciate you"
8. "I accept you in spite of your faults."
9. "I will always support you--I'm on your side!"
10. " I am concerned about your relationship with God--I pray for you every single day!"
11. " I have confidence in you--I expect good things from you."
12. "I trust you!"
13. "You are one of the most important things in my life!"
14. "You can do it!...I believe in you!"
15. "God loves you even more that I do!"
16. "Jesus loves you even when you are bad--though it makes Him very sad!"
17. "It is never too late to come home to God!
18. "When God forgives, The Bible says that He Forgets!" (Jeremiah 31:34)
19. "With God's help, you can change what you think, and what you feel!"
20. "A person can live right, please God, and have a wonderful life in spite of all of the bad things that have happened through family, or events."
21. "God longs for everyone to be saved, and to change the bad things in their lives--and He will Help those who seek."

Words of Truth That Will Set You And Your Family Free

1. R-"I'm sorry that I didn't know how to share at a deeper level with you kids. I will try in the future to tell you how I feel, and what my fears, hopes, and dreams are. I will try to tell you how much I love you, and how proud of you I am. I will try to share some of my personal doubts and hurts so that it will be safe for you to share some of yours. Please give me a new start, and be patient with me as I learn."

2. J- "I have frequently viewed my self and my life as inadequate, and anything that you say that in anyway reminds me of my faults, I become angry at you. I realize that my defensiveness and my ability to be hurt so easily probably came with me into our marriage, and that you are only a small reminder of my frustration with myself. I long for you to say all of the things that my parents did not know how to say to me. Things like: You have done a good job. We are very proud of you, Your grades this time don't mean that you are dumb, just that you haven't tapped into your real abilities yet. God has something great in store for you., You will do great things in the future, you can do it., You are a special and wonderful person, you are a real man, you have what it takes, you are a real woman, you are my precious and beautiful little girl.

3. S- I have had a bad habit for most of my life that I have let control me and damage my relationship with you. I am trying with God's help to win over this trap from Satan. Will you give me a new start, and help me to develop a real relationship with you? I'll be honest with you—I don't really know how to have a relationship—you'll have to help me.

4. D- " I feel so guilty for my lack of relationship with you. When people hint that it might be my fault, it makes me angry at myself and at them.---because I suspect it is true. I sometimes feel that it is too late, because you are grown up now. What can I do and say so that you would forgive me of all my mistakes, and give me another chance.

Words of Truth That Will Set You And Your Family Free
(Part 2)

5. D- I long to be "special" friends with you. I have been hurt by so many people in the past, that I subconsciously try not to get too close to anyone. That way they can't abandon and betray me like I have been treated in the past. It is funny! I long for real friends, and real relationships, but I can't allow people to be close. And I even resent them for not being close to me. Please don't give up on me. Please keep trying, even though it seems like I never respond. I want to—I am just scared.

6. S- I have been horribly wounded by some things that have happened to me in the past! I can't seem to tell anyone, because it is not safe. I feel like I am a big zero! I feel buried in shame, and guilt. It sometimes feels like I deserved all the things that hurt me. I push people away so they won't hurt me. But I need someone desperately.

7. S- I deserve never to be forgiven, and regardless of all the forgiveness verses the preacher reads, I can't seem to forgive myself. Please help me love myself

8. M- "I cannot stand who I am. I feel trapped by the things that I keep on doing. I am giving up on myself. Please convince me that there is still hope, and that you will still accept me.

9. J- I long to get rid of the burden of sin and guilt that I am carrying, but the thought of being rejected by all of you is more than I can bear. You could never forgive me, or love me, or respect me again. I guess I'll just have to suffer secretly, and keep pretending.

10. L- I long to feel loved first by someone. I want to be at the very top of someone's list. I hurt when I feel like an after thought or something to be dealt with after all of the "important things are done"

Some Essential Bible Lessons To Teach Your Children

(Parent the Heart, Not just the actions)

1. God loves you when you are good or bad.
2. God will punish you for being bad if you don't repent.
3. How to treat a spouse right when you don't feel like it, and when they don't deserve it
4. God deserves to be praised even when bad things happen—He is still on the throne and still in control.
5. Bad things will happen in life—expect them, and grow.
6. Trials can teach you good things.
7. Be a friend to sinners, but choose your companions from those who have Christian values.
8. Confess your faults—it is a strength not a weakness.
9. Take responsibility for your life—don't blame problems on others even if you have had a hard life.
10. Be bold in sharing the good news about Jesus.
11. Serve others—Go looking for those needing help.
12. Always consider the needs of others before your own.
13. Date only faithful Christians and then marry one!
14. Use your money and time for the Lord, not for yourself.
15. Learn to say, "I'm sorry, I was wrong, Please forgive me!
16. Say only good and positive things: we will be judged by Our words!
17. Be an Encourager
18. Be a Peacemaker
19. Try to find out what pleases the Lord
20. Learn to be content in all circumstances
    Learn to yield and submit to others—it is strength under control
21. Choose to be happy—it is a learned skill
22. Get your value from God, not from men
    God looks on the inside, not at beauty, brains, brawn, or bucks! He looks at your heart.
23. Learn How to share.

Essential Bible Lessons To Teach Your Children Continued

24. God is Real!—Creation gives evidence of His Power
25. There is absolute Truth which never changes—Seek It!
26. Things on earth are temporary—Don't waste your life
    seeking things that won't last! Material things will not,
    and can never satisfy you.
27. God's Commands are not Burdensome (God loves
    Us, and wants good things for his children)
28. The wages of sin is death—We all deserve to die
29. Death is nothing to be feared for a Christian
30. Love Bible Study—it is thrilling if you see its value
31. Singing Hymns is enjoyable and natural for a Christian
32. Love is not a feeling! It is a commitment to treat someone
    right regardless of feeling.
33. God Hates Divorce. It will not solve your problems.
34. Trust God even when you don't understand. We weren't
    meant to understand everything God does—Just to obey
35. Pray without ceasing—not just in Crisis—pray about the
    small things as well
36. Do not worry about having your basic needs met.
    If You are seeking God's Kingdom First. He will take
    care of you!
37. God will forgive anyone who really repents and asks
38. God never changes.
38. Material things will not, and can never satisfy you.
39. Failure isn't fatal! It is not too late to change
40. We are not trapped by our past mistakes
41. Just because you don't feel forgiven doesn't mean that
    God has not forgiven you

SCALING: INCREDIBLE COMMUNICATION TOOL

"Scaling" is a means of communication by using numbers on a scale to express feelings. On a scale of one to ten, one is low, poor, bad, etc. Ten represents great, wonderful, positive, etc. The numbers in between show how close you are to very good, or very bad.

The following are excellent questions for use in "scaling" on a regular basis:

1. How happy/fulfilled do you feel inside right now?
2. How was school/work for you today?
3. How much do you feel loved by me today?
4. How full is your emotional love bank right now?
5. How is your relationship with God today?
6. How fulfilling is our marriage to you today?
7. How much would you like to eat at _____ restaurant? How about _____ restaurant?
8. (To your spouse)What is your interest in a romantic relationship tonight?
9. How painful was the thing that happened? (Redefine the scale when needed)
10. How well do you like yourself?
11. How well do you think that others like you?
12. How angry or upset do you feel right now?
13. How strong were struggles with temptation today?
    * When a child or spouse is in the habit of answering the same question, you can understand a great deal about what is going on inside of them from day to day without a great deal of verbal communication. Compare the answers from today with yesterday, or last week.

Dr. Joe S. Brumfield, Nov 17, 1997

Fantastic Five For Fighting:
1. **Fight**
2. **Finish**
3. **Forgive**
4. **Flush**
5. **Forget**

God Forgives Forever! He Remembers our Sins No More (Hebrews 8:12)

Sometimes while fighting, we run out of ammunition (wet manure) to throw. Because we fear having no spears to throw back at our opponent, we get "historical" for more.   This means we leave the present argument and go back into our relationship history, and resurrect some old argument or disagreement.   Satan loves this sinful "recycling!"

This is sinful and foolish.   Make the commitment to stick to the problem you are on, and never bring up old "stuff!" Making a commitment to leave problems behind is very hard for a lot of people.

Rules: 1. Set an appropriate time and place. 2. No hitting below the belt

3. Write down one problem, and stick with that one only until finished.

4. Speak the truth in love, 5. Take Responsibility and say, "My part of this problem is...."   6. Hold Hands and Talk softly. 7. Pray, Pray, Pray!

The six "F" words; Fight, Finish, Forgive, Flush, Forget, and Forever are FANTASTIC!

Joe Brumfied   July 2008

36

Emptying Your Emotional Garbage

1. Almost everyone has hurts, anger, and frustrations stored up from the past.
2. God commands us to do what we can to solve differences with others as soon as we are aware of it (Mt 5, Mt 18)
3. Christians are required to deal with their anger before the day is over.
4. Reasons we hesitate to share our hurts and empty our emotional garbage:
   a. We don't want to get into a fight
   b. We wish to avoid the pain of reopening an old wound
   c. We fear the consequences of the other person punishing us in some way(sleep on the couch, etc.)
   d. We hope that as time passes the hurt will gradually go away
5. Reasons we must empty our emotional garbage anyway:
   a. God told us to!
   b. Stored hurts cause relationship cancer
   c. Stored hurts give the devil a foothold into our lives
   d. Our relationships will be better and more enjoyable
   e. We will be free from the burden of hurt and guilt

METHODS OF DEALING WITH EMOTIONAL GARBAGE:

1. <u>Sewer Contract</u>
   both parties in the relationship (husband,wife, etc.) Make a solemn agreement to never bring up old arguments and mistakes that have already been discussed dealt with, and forgiven.

"We promise that with God's help we will never again bring up old arguments, and issues from the sewer."

Signed_____ date_____
Signed_____ date_____
Witness_____ date_____

Things Parents Rarely Communicate Without Fighting:

*How Mom Needs To Say It:
1. One thing I need from you is affection, but I make that hard for you by being cold and resentful because I had to ask.
2. One thing I need from you is for you to love and cherish me, but I make that hard for you by being very stingy with my respect.
3. One thing I need from you is for you to put me first over your job and your hobbies, but I make that hard for you by putting the kids and the household jobs before you!
4. One thing I need from you is to know that you find me attractive and desirable, but I make that hard for you by not taking care of myself and pursuing you like I know you want.
5. One thing I need from you is for you to remember what I say to show me that you value my opinions and feelings. I make that hard for you by expecting you to think like a woman about details.

*How Dad Needs To Say it:
1. One thing I need is for you to trust my decision making about money, but I make that hard for you by sometimes being inconsiderate of your need for security.
2. One thing I need is for you to show me more respect and admiration as a man. I make that hard for you by not being more romantic, and by rarely helping around the house.
3. One thing I need is for you to let me lead, but I make that hard for you by not being more decisive, and leaving things undone until you are forced to make the decision, or get the joy done without me.
4. One thing I need from you is for you to romantically pursue me. I often make that difficult by expecting you to be romantic and flirty when you have never had that modeled growing up.
5. One thing I need from you is submission, but I make that hard for you by being overbearing in the way that I view you or expect that submission from you.

   *When you take a major part of the responsibility for not getting what you need, you allow your spouse to understand your need without being deeply wounded!
   ### Dr. Joe Brumfield Dec 2010

<u>Dumping Your Emotional Garbage</u>

Step One: **"One thing I want from you, but I'm hesitant to ask for is…**

Step Two: **One reason I make it hard for you to give me what I want is…**

<u>Reasons to empty the garbage:</u>
1. … Don't let the sun go down on your wrath
2. …If your brother sins against you, go to your brother, just between the two of you
3.…leave your gift at the altar—go and be reconciled with your brother

Help For Communicating Deep Feelings

1. It is hard for me to love you when _____.

2. I don't love _____ about myself.

3. I have a hard time trusting anyone because in the past
_____.

4. I probably have a hard time feeling loved and trusted because
_____.

5. I need to feel love from you because my parents _____.

6. One thing blocking me/us from feeling full love and acceptance from GOD is
_____.

7. If I felt totally loved, valued and accepted by GOD then I wouldn't need you to
_____.

8. I often struggle with deep selfishness because _____.

9. I have been refusing to treat you right until you meet all my needs. This is wrong because _____.

10. I feel so desperate to feel loved because
_____.

11. I don't like myself because _____.

12. I need my spouse to make me feel _____.

13. The devil wants me to react to this situation by
_____.

14. GOD wants me to react to _____
but I feel like _____.

15. One thing that is hindering me from meeting your needs is
_____.

16. One thing from the past that really hurt me/them was
_____.

SEWER CONTRACT

Because:
- Jesus taught us to deal with problems immediately, and
- Paul said that we are not to let the sun go down 'on our anger, and
- God forgives our sins, and "remembers them no more...
  (Matt. 5: 21-26, Matt. 18:15-20, Eph 4:26, Hebrew~ 8:12, Matt. 7:'12)

We, _____ and _____
on this the _____day of _____ in the year of our Lord _____,
in the sight of God, and the witnesses signed below, do faithfully promise the
following: things for each other:

a) We will share and pray about our frustrations, hurts, feelings, etc. before the end of the day, and we will

b) listen to the other's feelings without sharing our own until they feel that all their hurts and feeling's are emptied, and we will

c) gently resolve our differences while being kind and concerned for the other's feelings and we will

d) regularly say these magic words: "I am wrong, I am sorry, please forgive-me!!!", and we will

e) FLUSH RESOLVED DISAGREEMENTS AND HURTS DOWN THE EMOTIONAL TOILET AND NEVER BRING THEM UP AGAIN!

f) We will follow God's example by refusing to bring up old sins, problems, mistakes, hurts, and issues any more and we will   .

g) stick to the current issue so it can be quickly resolved and flushed away.

_____ & _____
Participant making promise   Participant making promise

_____   _____
witness   witness

Honesty Agreement

With God's help, We hereby, and from this moment on to pledge to honestly share our honest Feelings, needs, frustrations and hurts with each other. We will share these feelings honestly and sincerely on the outside at the same level we feel them on the inside. We promise to neither diminish, or enlarge these feelings.

Outside Show of Feelings, Hurts, and Emotions:

1   2   3   4   5   6   7   8   9   10

Inside true feelings of Hurts, and Emotions:

1   2   3   4   5   6   7   8   9   10

Jesus said, "Let your yes be yes, and your no, no. Anything beyond this comes from the evil one."

Deep Sharing Without Attacks!!

Rules:
1. No discussion for 24 hour
2. No disguised attacks:
    a. "I feel that you are a dirty rat"
    b. "I feel that it is all your fault"

Do it right by:

Saying "I feel_____(add a feeling word from column one)
when_____(share your feelings about some subject in
column 2)

Feeling Words	Subjects for Sharing Feelings
Frustrated	Job
Unloved	Kids
Abandoned	sex
Smothered	cooking
Hurt	television
Put down	friends
Ignored	laundry
Hated	my/your body
Devalued	family
Angry	health
Sad	future
Scared	finances
Overwhelmed	church
Disrespected	past
Cheated	car/driving
Overlooked	communication
Pressured/stressed	failures
Doubted	fights
Unwanted	aging
Unneeded	entertainment
Unaccepted	personality
Afraid	Habits

By Dr. Joe Brumfield April 5, 2006

Examples of "I feel" sharing

- I feel frustrated when...

- I feel appreciated when...

- I felt betrayed when...

- I feel hurt when...

- I feel abandoned when...

- I feel misused when...

- I feel unneeded when...

- I feel guilty when...

- I feel that I'm losing when...

- I feel left behind when...

- I feel forgotten when...

- I want to feel...

- I feel appreciated...

- I felt betrayed when...

- I felt unloved when...

- I feel disrespected when...

Dr. Joe Brumfield, March 06

Safe Sharing Contract

Honey,

    I can't tell you my hurts and frustrations any more because we always get in a fight. I really need you to know how I feel and I really need to know your hurts and frustrations so that we don't hurt each other so much. We need a special time where you and I agree to just listen to the other person **without responding** for at least one day

    When one of us feels a hurt or frustration we'll say "Safe Share?" The other will agree to listen without responding for at least one day by replying **"It is safe."**

We'll then share our feelings in one or two sentences by saying: **"It hurts my feelings when…,"** or **"I'm frustrated when…"**

And the other will respond by saying **"Thank you for sharing."** There will be no response or fighting. We'll will gently hold our spouse's feelings for a day And our "return fire" or "attack back" feelings may fade away.

The Bible says, "Be swift to hear, slow to speak, and slow to become angry."   Dr. Joe Brumfield, 2003

41

HELP IN EMPTYING YOUR EMOTIONAL HURTS

Dr. Joe Brumfield, March 1999

1. One thing that happened when I was young that hurt me was...

2. When I think of what happened to me in the past I feel...

3. I think that the Devil wants me to feel...

4. I am not comfortable telling people, but I wish people would...   for me.

5. One thing that bothers me about myself is...

6. I feel sad when...

7. It really hurts my feelings when...

8. One need I have that isn't being met is...

9. I need somebody who really cares about me to hold me accountable for...

10. One reason I get easily frustrated with people is...

11. I wish my parents had   ...

12. One thing that keeps me from being totally at peace with my dad is...

13. One thing that I ought to do, but am really hesitant to do to have a better relationship with my dad is...

14. On a scale of One to Ten, (one is low or bad & ten is high or good)
    a. My relationship with God right now feels like a(n)_____
    b. I feel loved by my family
    c. I like myself
    d. I think my fellow students value me

COMMUNICATION GAME QUESTIONS FOR
THE BOLD AND DARING
(Challenging Questions that reveal people's secret wishes)
by Brumfield, Brumfield, & Brumfield, May 29, 1998

Instructions: Without looking, pick a number between one and one hundred. Read and answer the question you have chosen. You may choose another person to answer the same question, or go on to the next person in line who will choose a number.

1. Name the top three character traits that you appreciate in other people.
2. What makes you happy?
3. What makes you excited?
4. What one thing "bugs" you most about about other people?
5. One thing I want to be remembered for when I die is...
6. Say something about: (pick one) families, divorce, God, true love, heaven, hell, death, money, presidents, government, music, politics, television, cars, houses, furniture, credit cards, morals, sin, the devil, friends, the past, the future...
7. My favorite thing about (pick one item from above) is....
8. One thing that bothers me about (pick one item from #6) is
9. One good thing about (pick one item from #6) is...
10. I am sad when...
11. I hurt when...
12. One thing that I regret from my past is...
13. One thing that I really need from the rest of you is...
14. I wish that I could improve...
15. I think the Devil is trying to get me by...
16. If I were the Devil, I would try to tempt (pick one person from the group) by ...
17. One of my worst faults is...
18. If my family were asked what I need to do to improve, they would likely say...
19. My idea of a fun family outing is...
20. I think the most enjoyable vacation would be...
21. I'm sad when...

22. I wish people would...
23. One unique thing about me that few people know is...
24. I think that one of my talents is ...
25. Tell something that you appreciate about someone else in the group around you, and tell why.
26. Share a quality that you wish you had or had more of.
27. I think that God may want me to ...
28. When I think about spiritual matters, I sometimes wonder if....
29. One thing from my childhood that was very sad was...
30. If I could change my parents, I would...
31. I really appreciate my parents for ...
32. If I weren't so shy about sharing my feelings, I would let my closest friends know...
33. I really long to feel God's closeness when...
34. I think that public school ...
35. I sometimes think that I would be happy if...
36. One interesting thing that I remember about a house I once lived in is...
37. One thing that really makes me nervous is...
38. My top two fears are...
39. My favorite (choose one:toothpaste. candy, cologne, perfume, shoes, cars, houses, hairstyle, musician, style of music, TV star, food, etc.) is_____ because...
40. My favorite biblical hero is_____ because...
41. I think kids should....
42. Many parents today make the mistake of...
43. One thing I need to be praying about more is ...
44. Some kids have trouble when they get older because...
45. The best families love each other because...
46. People who have the happiest marriages...
47. I feel sorry for people who...
48. One habit that I am wanting to change is...
49. God loves me because...
50. I have a hard time forgiving myself because...
51. Sometimes I don't like myself because...
52. Life doesn't seem fair because...
53. I sometimes wonder if God wants me to quit what I'm doing, and ...
54. I sometimes wonder about judgment, and think...

55. I wish my Mom would...
56. I wish my Dad would...
57. My parents could really improve their marriage if they would...
58. I sometimes don't feel forgiven by God because...
59. I wish God would...
60. My life would be better if...
61. If I could change one thing about my body...
62. One thing that I really like about myself is...
63. I am amazed that God will even forgive...
64. One thing about God's creation that amazes me is...
65. Every day I am so thankful that God...
66. One thing that I wish my friends would pray for me is...
67. If people knew the truth about me, they...
68. God has smiled on me in a special way by...
69. I get bored when...
70. One thing that I really fear is ...
71. The one thing that I enjoy doing the most with my family is...
72. The one thing I wish my family wouldn't do is...
73. One thing that I wish my dad would tell me is...
74. One thing that I wish my mom would tell me is...
75. I sometimes think that my parents only love me if
76. I sometimes think that may parents care more about

_____ than about_____.
77. I can't believe that my parents put up with me when

I...
78. One thing that I wish my parents would have been more strict on was...
79. My parents were afraid to...
80. Some people might think that my parents didn't value spiritual things as much as_____because...
81. I wish my parents had/would taught/teach me to

_____.
82. My parents spent _____time with me when I was younger, and I wish that...
83. I really appreciate the sacrifices that my parents made for me because...
84. One new thing that I have learned recently about the Bible is...
85. The difference in a person who exceeds the speed

limit without a cruise control, and the person who intentionally sets their cruise above the speed limit is...

86. One thing that I really want to do, but I have doubts about whether God really wants me to is...

87. If everything I do is supposed to bring Glory to God, does that mean that when I _____ it has to bring glory to God also?

88. One things that my friends pressure me to do, that I don't really want to do is...

89. When I lose my friends, I feel...

90. Why does God allow things to happen like...

91. It is really hard for me to tell my parents about the negative influences at school because...

92. I wish the Bible would give a more clear answer about...

93. One thing that some Christians do that causes me to stumble or struggle some is...

94. Some of my Christian friends seem to care about God some, but they don't seem to understand that...

95. I wish _____ would tell me more how much they love and appreciate me.

96. I sometimes feel hurt inside because...

97. The one of the fruits of the Spirit that I need to grow most in is ...

98. One Bible question that I would like an answer for is...

99. The lost person whom I long to be saved the most is...

100. I want to praise God because...

by Brumfield, Brumfield, & Brumfield, May 29, 1998

Messages from Substance Abusers:

"This joint, or whiskey bottle, or pill is my desperate attempt to communicate something that I can't say. If you take my stuff away from me, you have not solved the real problem. My real problem is underneath the message I am trying to communicate to you." --Dr. Joe's interpretation of their message

    1. "I hurt!"

    2. "I want to die!"

    3. "Let's party!"

    4. "I am outraged!"

    5. "Please notice me!"

    6. "I am afraid!"

From <u>Dying to Tell</u> by Lewis, Dodd, & Tippens 1992

What Cultural Messages Are Actually Shaping Your Child's Heart?
More Powerful than Words, and more Subtle than Preaching

1. Religion is a private matter
2. One must have money to fit in
3. Only weak people do right (they don't have the guts to "brave" sin
4. Success at your job =success at home
5. Don't be a conformist and do right; be unique and be "wild"
6. Everything revolves around me
7. Your soul doesn't matter if your body looks good
8. No commitment can't be broken
9. Following God's rules does not bring success
10. Outer image is everything--what's inside has little meaning
11. Keeping up with the Jones is more important than evangelizing the Jones
12. Other people's pain or misfortune is funny
13. It's shameful to stay home and raise children
14. If you're popular, you can get away with anything
15. It's OK to honor violence and sex if you do it through movies and music
16. Christians are a pain, they are ignorant, and are bigots
17. If you are poor, it's OK to hate rich people
18. If you were brought up in a bad neighborhood, or in a dysfunctional family, you can't help hurting others
19. A person can pay money to avoid the consequences of wrong, sinful, or illegal behavior
20. Movie ratings teach that sex and bad language are not dangerous
21. Academic success is more important than spiritual success
22. It is not lust if one views an image online—instead of a real person
23. If you aren't married or engaged when you graduate, something is wrong with you
24. One major goal in life is to be better than anyone else
25. Always justify yourself and explain why things are not your fault--people will think more of you
26. Judge no one--be tolerant of everyone's beliefs and opinions-- after all, truth is different for everyone.

TEACHERS ARE NOT TEACHING WHAT THEY THINK
Dr. Joe Brumfield

Fact: Most learning does not occur in the classroom, and lecture is the least effective method of teaching!

We think we are teaching math, english, science, and history.   We are actually teaching many more important lessons which answer the following questions:

a. How can I get people to like me?

b. What makes me valuable to others?

c. What makes me happy?

d. What is the purpose of life?

e. What image of myself should I project regardless of what is true?

f. What is important in life?

g. How can I win over everyone else?

h. Will nice clothes make people like me?

i. Is inner or exterior beauty most important?

j. How important is having a nice car for having people value you.

k. Is family time or sports time more valuable?

l. Is it more important to go to bed on a school night, or on Saturday night?

m. Will playing sports make me valued and accepted?

n. How much am I worth if I am not beautiful or handsome?

o. Will my dad accept me if I make the team?

p. Is chapel or the ball game more important?

Lessons Parents Are Accidentally Teaching Children:
1. Materialism--get all you can to be happy
2. Entertain yourself--do, eat, watch, whatever turns you on
3. Be Sexual--get whatever pleasure you can
   Proof: we choose entertainment for pleasure
   rather than for spiritual value
4. You can't count on anyone or anything--nothing is the same, parents divorce, families move, cars, jobs, and houses change.
5. There is no set right or wrong-each person determines what is right for them.
6. There is no absolute truth
7. Things are wrong only if you get caught and convicted
8. All spouses cheat--cheating is normal--expect it
9. No one will love you forever--for the real you!
10. If someone does love you--it won't last.
11. A person is not valuable unless they are handsome or beautiful.
12. A person is not desirable unless they are rich
13. If you lose a boyfriend or girlfriend, life isn't worth living.
14. Keeping up with the Jones is more important than bringing the Jones to Jesus: we buy $150 shoes to fit in, instead of buying $60 shoes and giving the rest for evangelism, etc.
15. Having people like you, and not offending people is more important than standing up for truth.

Default Messages of Parents

"Pardon, Your Values Are Showing"

We received about 15 inches of rain each year in New Mexico, and sometimes half of it seemed to come on the same day. I'll never forget riding in that station wagon with my three brothers and five sisters on the way to the church building. Why were we going? Nobody would fault us if we didn't make it. The water was too high. It was coming in the doors of the car. I don't remember the sermon, and I'm not even sure who the preacher was then, but I'll never forget my dad pulling the car with the tractor on the way to the church house. I learned a lesson that day that a thousand sermons couldn't teach. I learned how important it was to worship God and encourage the saints. My dad probably didn't think he was teaching. He was just driving the tractor. His true values were showing---and they were contagious. I caught them!

Children are more likely to perceive a parents "real" love for God by watching attitudes in the car on the way to the Church building than by watching them on the pew! The "unintentional message" is more powerful! Even if children are wrong, they still have a perception of their parents' attitudes and motives for worship. You can tell if parents are excited about going to worship with the saints, or if they are going out of duty to get their ticket punched. Lets see... "took the Lord's Supper ...Check...gave of my means...Check...sang and prayed...Check..." No, you didn't say these things, but your children are watching you like a hawk! They see every smile. They learn more from your voice tone than from your words. Your child's perceptions of your attitudes are stored as a part of their own values. Thank God my parents sang praises in the car. It was an unintentional default message but it came through loud and clear. They took us to church services so we would learn to love God, but I learned about praising God by watching them. The little video camera in my head never ran out of film. The video camera in your children's minds never stops either.

Some parents are foolish enough to think that their intentional messages are the main ones learned. They are so surprised when their children grow up with different views and values than the ones they "talked about." Children are incredibly perceptive in seeing "true parent values" This perception is their automatic default setting. If parents, grandparents, friends and neighbors sit in the stands to clap and cheer for them at a ball game, but nobody cheers when they memorize the books of the bible, or learn their Sunday school lesson---something big happens! They learn that sports and entertainment are more important than spiritual things--regardless of what parents say with their words. Talk is cheap in our culture. Our true priorities show in our deeds, and in our checkbooks. How we spend our time, attention, and money is an indicator of the values we are teaching our children by default.

Children watch what we do when we are free to do what we wish. Our children learn more about our love for God when we sing hymns doing the dishes, than when we sit on the pew. They know inside that people are expected to sing on the pew. They also know that mom sings about God's Amazing Grace at home--just because she wants to. What would happen if you invited some Christian friends over to sing hymns---just for the pure enjoyment of it? Your children know what you really enjoy. They memorize every message from the movies you watch and every book you read. Just watching it or enjoying it sends a message that it's OK! When you laugh--they know what a Christian should laugh at. When you hold the remote control, they notice how long you linger on each channel as you surf. Watch out, your true values are showing.

Default Messages of Parents Continued

Most of our default messages are taught when our children see us making choices about life. If I praise my son more for throwing a touchdown pass, than I do for his prayer, than I have taught him a lesson by default. I never would purposefully teach him that sports are more important than prayer. If I choose to take my son out of school a day early to go on our family vacation, but never take him out of school to go to a gospel meeting etc. , my true priorities are showing. My "preaching" will not undo the message that he has seen with his very own eyes.

If I require that my children go to bed early on a "school night," but say nothing about going to bed early on a Saturday night, what lesson have they learned by default? Some parents wonder why their children care so little for spiritual things. They are sticklers about washing hands, brushing teeth, taking vitamins, and not drinking from someone else's glass, but say very little about the spiritual germs that come into their children's minds thru the media. We're teaching them clearly that physical germs can kill you, so what is the default message about the comparative danger spiritual germs? We are teaching that it is fine to "drink from the toilet" spiritually speaking!

Children watch how much money parents spend at the store, and they also watch parents put money into the collection plate on Sunday. They know when you sacrifice for something and when you don't. Consider what an incredible message was sent when the widow gave to God the only money she had to live on. A different message is sent by a parent who gives God $100 when they have $1000 in the bank than is sent by a parent who gives $100 when they have nothing else. Sacrifice sends powerful messages to children that can be taught no other way.

A radar detector on the dash of dad's car sends the message: "It's OK to break the law if you can get away with it. Telling someone on the phone that Mom isn't home when she really is says that deception is OK if you have a good reason. Laughing at an off-color joke from a late night television show may teach that Christians can enjoy "good, clean, dirty fun." Watching impure and immoral actions on television may send the message that "it is OK to think about it, enjoy it, and visualize it, as long as you don't do it. Children watch to see which things cause a parent to turn the television off, and what they watch. I learned so much when my dad turned the television off when it was time for the family devotional--even if an exciting movie was on. We learned his true priorities. Watching my dad kneel on the living room floor to pray every night left a deep impression about who and what was worth bowing to in this life. When parents are constantly admiring nice cars, and nice houses, why are they so surprised when their child chooses a money profession instead of a missionary profession? It's because their true values were showing.

Dr. Joe Brumfield teaches Bible courses and Marriage and Family Therapy at Harding University. He enjoys local preaching as well as holding Marriage Enrichment and Parenting seminars for Churches around the country.

Heart Pain Locator

Dr Joe Brumfield April 26. 2007

<u>Explanation:</u> **Their deposits in my emotional bank predict my reaction to them and to many other things in my life! It helps explain why I act the way I do.**

<u>Instructions:</u> **Place a number between 1 and 10 (to represent your feelings) below each category. 1 is very little and 10 is much.**

	Spouse	sibling	1st child	2nd Child	Mom	Dad	Boss	Co-worker
I Feel Loved By them	9	3	10	8	10	8	6	3
I Feel Needed By them								
I Feel Respected By them								
I Feel Accepted By them								
I Feel they are Meeting My Needs								
I Feel They Are helping me Reach my Personal Goal of Feeling Loved, needed, Wanted, valued, and accepted by other people								

Open Ended Sentences to Build a New Foundation
(help people empty some hurt before trying to do therapy/surgery)

I am guilty of hurting you by...

I'm sorry that I made you feel unloved when I...

I wish I had never...

If I could go back, one mistake that I would not make is...

One thing that I have needed that I never could get through to you is...

I know that God would have wanted me to...

I know that you needed me to do more...

It would have also helped if I had done less...

I don't really deserve to be forgiven for...

I know that you really needed me to...

I believe that I hurt God when I...

I think that God wants me to ...

I have been jealous of...

I was wrong to expect_____without letting you know.

Dr. Brumfield

Sept 7, 2001

What Couples Are Really Saying:

1. You don't remember what I tell you =You are not making me feel loved.---Don't I count??

   2. You don't consciously make it a point to do little things that make me think that you are thinking of me

   3. When you go golfing, fishing, shopping, hunting when you don't spend any time with me, I feel unloved

   4. Every choice you make—I think, "does this show how important I am to you?"

   5. Every word you say, " I ask myself: does this show how much he/she cares about me?"

   6. I fall asleep every time I sit down might = I am depressed
       a. I am avoiding uncomfortable interactions with you
       b. I feel greatly stressed by what is expected of me in life

   7. When you say, "You are never gonna be happy," I feel Like you don't have any hope for our future

   8. When you make me feel that I am a total inconvenience to your life, and that I cramp your style—I feel that you wish that you hadn't married me.

   9. I want to feel like you are glad you married me. (tell me often)

   10. I want to feel that you want me sexually even when you are too tired—we don't have to have sex, I just want to feel wanted, needed and loved.

   11. People have rejected me in the past, and I am almost expecting it—maybe that is why I am touchy and read more negative into things than is really there.

   12. I am feeling put down and attacked by the world, and I desperately need you to make me feel safe and secure— I look for this love, safety, and security in every word, every glance, and every action from you.

   13. I need your support desperately, but I am not in the situation where I have the strength to ask.

   14. I need your gentle strength and support—you are so strong— Nobody else can make me feel safe and strong
   Other than you. I'm sorry that I am too weak to meet all of your needs. Thank you for being my hero!!

   15. I thank God for you. I look forward to growing with you and Building a growing relationship with God together.

Dr. Joe Brumfield Oct 2001

Discussions With Parents

Both Parent and son or daughter should share answers to the following:

1. Some things that you have done that make me feel loved are...
2. Rate in order of importance to you the following life goals:___ personal comfort,___a feeling of accomplishment,___a successful family,___spiritual growth, ___having fun in life, ___good health, ___safety and security, ___knowing you are loved, ___success and esteem in the eyes of friends, ___ being able to own some of the nice things in life. (Discuss Why)
3. One of the ways that the Devil has tried to destroy me is:
4. Some of the things I really appreciate you for are...
5. I sometimes wonder if God wants me to stop following my personal goals and...
6. I regret that I haven't told you more that...
7. I am really sorry that I...
8. Some hurts that I received in the past or from my family that I haven't told you much about are...
9. One fear I have about my future is...
10. One lie I have believed about myself (from past hurts) is...
11. On a scale of 1-10 (1 is lowest, 10 is highest) my present relationship with God is...
12. If I move my relationship one notch higher I would need to...
13. One question I have about God, the Bible, or Spiritual things is:
14. One thing that I wish my you/myparents had done differently with me is...
15. If my family was asked what things I need to do to improve myself they would probably say:
16. I may have buried it inside, but It hurt me when...
17. I don't feel loved and appreciated as much if my family doesn't ...
18. One quality I wish I had more of is...
19. God loves me/doesn't like me much because...
20. I sometimes don't feel forgiven by God because...
21. One thing I really want to do, but have doubts about is...
22. The lost person whom I most long to be saved is_____because:
23. I sometimes feel sad/frustrated inside when...
24. I need you to empty out all of your past hurts and frustrations toward me so that we Can....
25. I think that Satan wants you to hold all the little and big hurts/frustrations inside instead of sharing them because...
26. Some things I need you to pray about for me are...
27. Some things I regret from my past are...
28. Some ways I need you to do to encourage me spiritually are...

Discussions With Outstanding People
by Dr. Joe Brumfield

Name_____

Person Interviewed_____

Time spent in discussion_____

Instructions:

Both People must share answers to the following questions with an outstanding single person of the opposite sex. Write down what you learn from the discussion.

1. What is one thing you hope to do differently than your parents did with marriage or children?

2. Rate in order of importance to you the following life goals:___ personal comfort,___a feeling of accomplishment,___a successful family,___spiritual growth, ___having fun in life, ___good health, ___safety and security, ___knowing you are loved, ___success and esteem in the eyes of friends, ___ being able to own some of the nice things in life. (Discuss Why)

3. One of the ways that the Devil has tried to destroy me is:

4. I think churches would be better if:

5. I sometimes wonder if God wants me to stop following my personal goals and...

6. I think that a lot of kids have problems because parents...

7. I think it might be hard to live with a husband/wife (opposite of person answering) who...

8. One thing I will do to make sure my family stays faithful to God is...

9. One fear I have about my future is...

10. Describe what a perfect spouse would act like, do, etc.:

11. On a scale of 1-10 (1 is lowest, 10 is highest) rate your present relationship with God.

12. What would you have to do to move it up a notch?

13. One question I have about God, the Bible, or Spiritual things is:

14. One thing that I wish my parents had done differently with me is...

15. If my family was asked what things I need to do to improve myself they would probably say:

16. One little thing my parents/family/friends have done or said in the last month that made me feel loved was:

17. I don't feel loved and appreciated as much if my family doesn't …

18. One quality I wish I had more of is...

19. God loves me/doesn't like me much because...

20. I sometimes don't feel forgiven by God because...

21. One thing I really want to do, but have doubts about is...

22. The lost person whom I most long to be saved is_____because:

23. I sometimes feel hurt inside when...

24. Regardless of how much money I make, I think the standard of living God wants me to live at is...

25. One things my parents need/needed to differently in their relationship is/was...

26. One way I wish my parents had been more strict on me is...

27. One thing I regret from my past is...

28. It will be more important to me for my spouse (someday) to give lots of loving touch (non-sexual), or remember me with small gifts, or spend lots of one-one one quality time with me, or give me lots of verbal appreciation, or do good deeds for me. Explain:

Date_____

We the undersigned promise that with the help of God, that we will do our best never to use the following phrases in the future years of our lifetime:

"What's wrong with you?"

"I can't do anything to please you"

"You get what you deserve!"

"You're impossible!"

"I don't know why I put up with you!"

"I can do whatever I like!"

"If you don't like it, you can just leave!"

"Turnabout's fair play"

"If you really love me, you'd do this"

"You deserve a dose of your own medicine!"

"What's your problem?"

_____
Husband

_____
Wife

_____
Witness   Dr. Joe Brumfield, Searcy, AR

QUESTIONS TO ASK YOURSELF BEFORE ANY PURCHASE

1. Do I really need it?
2. Will It improve my ability to bring others to Jesus?
3. Is this the best time to buy?
4. How will it effect my family spiritually?
5. How will it effect my future?
6. Have I researched the item?
7. Does it have any upkeep?
8. Will it increase or decrease in value?
9. How will it effect my use of time?
10. Would God want me to buy it?
11. Will it help me get closer to my eternal goals?
12. Can I purchase it at a better price somewhere else?

Financial Suggestions for Christian Success in Stewardship:

1. Do not carry more than $20 in cash at a time.
2. Always shop from a pre-prepared list.
3. Stay in the store only as long as absolutely necessary to buy the things on your list.
4. Always have a full meal just before purchasing groceries.
5. Do not purchase anything before you have the <u>cash on hand!</u>
6. Pay for everything with cash.
7. Do not use credit if you do not have the money on hand.
8. Cut up your credit cards on the month that you can not pay the bill in full.
9. Always discuss larger ticket items with your spouse before buying.
10. Wait two weeks after your decision, before the actual purchase.
11. Do not window shop; even in catalogs.
12. Live by a budget.
13. Live on one income even if you have two. Those who get used to two incomes, are rarely able to go back to one.
14. Buy the things you need out of season, and on sale.

Dr. Joe Brumfield--April, 1998

To Save....or Not to Save

Couple "A"

NOW

$40,000/yr. starting income

-lives on $40,000/yr. for first 5 yrs.

-apartment rent $400/mo.

-purchases: bed, couch, table,
 TV, stereo, washer/dryer

- transportation - 2 jobs, 2 cars
  buy new vehicles - $900/mo. with
  payments and insurance

5 YEARS LATER

- no money saved
- takes out a 30 yr. mortgage
- ends up paying $360,000 for house
- wife has to keep working
- extra cost of childcare ($400/mo.)
- still needs two cars and would like
  newer vehicles, but can't afford them

Couple "B"

NOW

- $40,000/yr. starting income
- lives on $20,000/yr. for first 5 yrs.
- apartment rent - minimum
- purchases: not many - borrows
  furniture from family or buys used,
  washes clothes at laundromat
- transportation - drives older, used
  cars - no extensive payments

5 YEARS LATER

3 bdr. house in nice Searcy area - approx. $100,000

- has saved $100,000
- pays cash for 3 bdr. house
- pays $100,000 for house
- wife can now stay home
- wife at home with kids
- can now finance a new car and
  only needs one vehicle since wife
  stays at home

Qualities of Strong and Healthy Families: Specific Plans For Making It Happen

1. <u>They have a spiritual foundation and lifestyle</u>- pray together daily, morning and evening; family devotional weekly: (read a Bible verse together weekly and discuss it), become a member of a church, visit a church group; do a service project together; posting scriptures in the home;

2. <u>They admit their problems and search for help</u>- keep an accountability journal: (write things I want to work on, my struggles for the day); Father leads in admitting problems to create a safe environment.

3. <u>They regularly compliment and encourage each other</u>- give at least three compliments per day; one when they come in the door; one before bed, change criticisms to compliments, leave encouragement notes to the family; learn how to accept compliments (say thank you, etc)

4. <u>They work at communicating and listening to each other.</u> (Communication is balanced, direct, and open)

5. <u>They teach and share responsibility</u>- chart jobs that are to be done in the house (include consequences and rewards); connect natural consequences to certain behaviors; emphasize empathy(when the car drives up with groceries from the store the kids are required to come out of the house and say, "how may I help you?"

6. <u>They consciously sacrifice other good things to spend quality and quantity time together</u>-one hour per week, give up routine activities to spend time with family; brainstorm monthly for family ideas; prioritize list for top four; do at least one per week

7. <u>They have a firm parental coalition and clear family rules.</u> (Expectations are clear)- Mom and Dad cooperate in setting rules, they are on the same page; speak to each other often; both know where the kids are; set parameters together; family should have meetings to go over the rules; set a regular family meeting time followed by family fun time; Talk with kids about things that should be changed; punishments and rewards; post the rules on the fridge; any emergency announcements are posted on the tv screen

8. <u>They have quality family table time and conversation</u>- decide what quality time is…movies?; make sure all are there, no TV, no cell phones or phone calls, facing each other; basket on the table…questions, discussion subjects…one chosen at each meal; create family discussion; (the more time you spend with your family, the less chance of substance abuse)

9. <u>They value formal and informal family rituals and traditions.</u>
Spend time creating your own traditions, dinner at table nightly; every third weekend do something as a family

10. <u>They share adaptability and flexibility in family function</u>-report events with a family calendar; agree on different activities, compromise and discuss; deemphasize "I" want or "I need"; No negative talk (or "shut up Kid"), but the parent signal tells when the kids are being selfish; celebrate the accomplishments of the child that sacrificed the most that week

11. <u>They demonstrate affection with other family members.</u>
Hugs, kind words, smiles, encouraging voice tones…

12. <u>They honor their older family members</u>-spend time; listen to stories; schedule monthly extended communication.

13. <u>Every family member is valued</u>, and their contributions are seen as essential-write positive statements about family members; have a post board; write so many positive comments weekly.

14. <u>Physical and emotional security and support are provided for each member</u>-, "I love you" daily, notes; be kind even when they aren't giving to you.

15. <u>They are hospitable and have surrounding rings of friends and relatives</u>- have game night; friend night; family night at different peoples houses monthly

16. <u>Each family member has the ability to grow and change</u>- keep a record of growth and changes; mark on the wall more than vertical growth; prayer journal; family albums; behavior charts

17. <u>Each one has the ability to accept help when appropriate and the ability for self-help</u>-admit you can't do it all; whole family writes their strengths and weaknesses; write when you asked and accepted help; practice offering and accepting help; Dad models by asking directions to make mom feel loved, even thought He knows he could find the way

18. <u>The family has the ability to use a crisis or hurtful experience as a means for growth</u>- communicate—talk about your feelings and needs; Watch for the dead elephant—don't avoid the issues—deal with stuff as it comes up; Show the belief that crisis and trouble are a part of life to be expected!!

19. <u>The family has a clear commitment to unity, cooperation, and loyalty</u>- place ideas in a box—the family does it together; draw one out monthly; Everyone has to be involved with the family project because it is a "family" activity!

20. <u>There is the ability to build and maintain relationships outside the family.</u>
Encourage the whole family to be involved in extracurricular activities of various kinds: youth, church, outings with friends; friends over; mom and dad date double; out to eat   Dr. Joe Brumfield Harding University (adapted from research from Curran, 1983; Stinnet, 1979; Lewis, et al., 1976; Howard, 1978; Satir, 1972; Otto, 1975)

God's ABC's For Training Children

A. Parents Must be clearly in charge
B. Children must follow the parents rules
C. There must be clear rules and communication
D. Parents are to be respected in public and private
E. Parents should not push children so hard that the children are frustrated
F. Fathers are primarily responsible to make sure that the children are trained in spiritual matters

Ephesians 6:1-4 (English-NIV)

1 Children, obey your parents in the Lord, for this is right.

2 "Honor your father and mother"--which is the first commandment with a promise--

3 "that it may go well with you and that you may enjoy long life on the earth."

4 Fathers, do not exasperate your children; instead, bring them up in the training and instruction of the Lord.

G. If your parenting style is making your kids discouraged, then you are doing something wrong!

Colossians 3:20-21 (English-NIV)

20 Children, obey your parents in everything, for this pleases the Lord.

21 Fathers, do not embitter your children, or they will become discouraged.

H. A parents emotional health is directly connected to how their children act. If you do not carefully train your children, you will likely be a sad and discontent parent.

Proverbs 10:1 (English-NIV)

The proverbs of Solomon: A wise son brings joy to his father, but a foolish son grief to his mother

I. A parent should give clear instructions, and then make sure that they are followed. Never make threats that you are not willing to carry out.

Proverbs 13:1 (English-NIV)

1 A wise son heeds his father's instruction, but a mocker does not listen to rebuke.

J. Disobedience must be punished. Punishment is often painful. Parents who are too weak to punish disobedience when children are smaller will reap what they sow.   If you can't control your child at 5, don't expect to be in charge when your children are 15.

Proverbs 13:24

He who spares the rod hates his son, but he who loves him is careful to discipline him.

K. Discipline can be a sign that you truly love your children

Hebrews 12:5-11 (English-NIV)

5 And you have forgotten that word of encouragement that addresses you as   sons: "My son, do not make light of the Lord's discipline, and do not lose heart when he rebukes you,

6 because the Lord disciplines those he loves, and he punishes everyone he accepts as a son."

7 Endure hardship as discipline; God is treating you as sons. For what son is not disciplined by his father?

8 If you are not disciplined (and everyone undergoes discipline), then you are illegitimate children and not true sons.

9 Moreover, we have all had human fathers who disciplined us and we respected them for it. How much more should we submit to the Father of our spirits and live!

10 Our fathers disciplined us for a little while as they thought best; but God disciplines us for our good, that we may share in his holiness.

11 No discipline seems pleasant at the time, but painful. Later on, however, it produces a harvest of righteousness and peace for those who have been trained by it.

L. Grandchildren are something to be proud of
   Don't forget parenting responsibilities of Grandparents
   Deut 4:9; Proverbs 17:6 (English-NIV)
Children's children are a crown to the aged, and parents are the pride of their children.

M. Teach children wisdom, and someday, you'll be glad!
   Proverbs 17:25 (English-NIV)
   A foolish son brings grief to his father and bitterness to the one who bore him.

N. All of your life's accomplishments will seem like gravel in your mouth if you fail to take the time to raise wise kids
   Proverbs 19:13-18 (English-NIV)
   3 A foolish son is his father's ruin, and a quarrelsome wife is like a constant dripping.

O. Parents who think they "love" their child too much to discipline them will share responsibility for the child's spiritual and/or physical death
   Pro 19:18 Discipline your son, for in that there is hope; do not be a willing party to his death.

P. Parents should both require, and be worthy of great respect from their children. To allow your child to disrespect his or her parents is to curse their view of all adult authority.
   Proverbs 20:20 (English-NIV)
   If a man curses his father or mother, his lamp will be snuffed out in pitch darkness.

Q. Children tend to be in their old age what their parents trained them to be in their youth. Perfect parents and a perfect environment do not guarantee perfect children. Satan is at work, and children have free will. Adam and Eve had the perfect Father (God), and a perfect environment (the garden) They still sinned, and were separated from God.

Proverbs 22:6-15 (English-NIV)

6 Train a child in the way he should go, and when he is old he will not turn from it.

R. Kids seem to do some foolish things just because they are kids. If parents do not pull this weed while it is little, it will grow into a tree that can't be pulled.

Proverbs 22:15 Folly is bound up in the heart of a child, but the rod of discipline will drive it far from him.

S. Parents that view spanking as too harsh of a discipline method may be minimizing the dangers of refusing discipline: your child could lose his or soul if they don't change. Serious diseases require distasteful medicine and painful surgery--but it is worth it if it saves your life. Ignore this cancer at your own risk!

Proverbs 23:13-35 (English-NIV)

13 Do not withhold discipline from a child; if you punish him with the rod, he will not die.

14 Punish him with the rod and save his soul from death. [1]

15 My son, if your heart is wise, then my heart will be glad;

16 my inmost being will rejoice when your lips speak what is right.

17 Do not let your heart envy sinners, but always be zealous for the fear of the LORD.

18 There is surely a future hope for you, and your hope will not be cut off.

19 Listen, my son, and be wise, and keep your heart on the right path.

T. Parents must make sure that children don't make friends with those who have bad spiritual or physical habits.

Proverbs 23:20 Do not join those who drink too much wine or gorge themselves on meat,

21 for drunkards and gluttons become poor, and drowsiness clothes them in rags.

22 Listen to your father, who gave you life, and do not despise your mother when she is old.

23 Buy the truth and do not sell it; get wisdom, discipline and understanding.

24 The father of a righteous man has great joy; he who has a wise son delights in him.

25 May your father and mother be glad; may she who gave you birth rejoice!

21. Sons need lots of clear teaching about how do deal with lustful desires.

26 My son, give me your heart and let your eyes keep to my ways,

27 for a prostitute is a deep pit and a wayward wife is a narrow well.

28 Like a bandit she lies in wait, and multiplies the unfaithful among men.

U. Kids must be taught about the dangers of alcohol

Proverbs 23:29 Who has woe? Who has sorrow? Who has strife? Who has complaints? Who has needless bruises? Who has bloodshot eyes?

30 Those who linger over wine, who go to sample bowls of mixed wine.

31 Do not gaze at wine when it is red, when it sparkles in the cup, when it goes down smoothly!

32 In the end it bites like a snake and poisons like a viper.

33 Your eyes will see strange sights and your mind imagine confusing things.

34 You will be like one sleeping on the high seas, lying on top of the
   rigging.
35 "They hit me," you will say, "but I'm not hurt! They beat me, but I
   don't feel it! When will I wake up so I can find another drink?"

**V. Children do not need to be left alone. They need constant
   parental attention, and training. Parents who let the
   television or the school programs babysit their children
   will reap children who have television spiritual values.**
Proverbs 29:15-22 (English-NIV)
15 The rod of correction imparts wisdom, but a child left to himself
   disgraces his mother.
16 When the wicked thrive, so does sin, but the righteous will see their
   downfall.
17 Discipline your son, and he will give you peace; he will bring
   delight to your soul.
18 Where there is no revelation, the people cast off restraint; but
   blessed is he who keeps the law.
19 A servant cannot be corrected by mere words; though he
   understands, he will not respond.
20 Do you see a man who speaks in haste? There is more hope for a
   fool than for him.

**W. Parents who give their kids just about everything their
   little hearts desire are likely building hearts that think they
   must have what they want to be happy. They will not learn
   that happiness is a choice--they will be miserable when they
   are older and cannot have what they want when they want.
   Woe to you whose child marries a child that was pampered
   from their youth. You will pray for crop failure, but you
   will reap what you have sown.**
   Proverbs 23:21 If a man pampers his servant from youth, he will
   bring grief in the end.

X. God gives a clear prescription for raising children that are faithful to him. It requires an incredible faith from parents first, and then it requires massive amounts of time with children. Your children's spiritual values will be in direct proportion to the daily time that they spend with different value teaching mediums: Parents(15 minutes), peers(8 hrs), television(3-4 hrs), music (3-6 hrs), school teachers(7hrs), coaches(1 hr)...

Deuteronomy 6:1-10 (English-NIV)

4 Hear, O Israel: The LORD our God, the LORD is one. [1]

5 Love the LORD your God with all your heart and with all your soul and with all your strength. 6 These commandments that I give you today are to be upon your hearts. 7 Impress them on your children. Talk about them when you sit at home and when you walk along the road, when you lie down and when you get up.

8 Tie them as symbols on your hands and bind them on your foreheads. 9 Write them on the doorframes of your houses and on your gates.

Y. Parenting is apparently a full time job requiring an incredible Amount of teaching time to build spiritual children.

Z. Pray without ceasing! Redeem the Time, because we live in evil times.

What If I caused them to be the way they are

- What if my kids are depressed and have low self esteem because I didn't compliment them when they were young?
- What if my wife is overweight because I rarely complimented her when she was eating right and exercising?
- What if your wife is as exciting as your regular complements are to her: "You are an exciting and thrilling woman!!!"

- What if your wife views herself through your eyes, and you are actually programming her on a daily basis!

- What if your husband has given up on anything except watching TV and eating because he has little hope for anything better in the future. What if he sees himself as a lazy, incompetent, "inadequate" man because that is what he hears (reading between the lines) in his wife's voice tone, questions, words, and rare praise.

- If your facts and perceptions are faulty and wrong, then your expectations will be off!

- You have been programmed to expect misery.. programmed to expect that , "Now that I'm over 50, life is downhill from here…"
- REPROGRAM YOURSELF!!!

Lessons I Want to teach My Children Before I Die
Dr Joe Brumfield Sept 15, 2001

1. Praying to God is as natural and important as breathing and eating
2. Real men and women confess their faults
3. Choose to love a spouse that seems unlovable
4. Forgive yourself of the things God has already forgiven
5. Do not live in the past (failures or successes)
6. Enjoy giving to God and others
7. Visit and encourage sick people (it's like visiting God)
8. Teach the lost--it's extremely urgent
9. Study the Bible for fun, and in a serious way
10. Learn to resolve conflict: compromise, surrender, apologize...
11. Take responsibility for your own mistakes-don't make excuses
12. Learn to give and take loving sincere rebuke
13. Search for and help spiritually hurting people
14. Seek out and encourage the lonely
15. Work at any job you have --as if working for the Lord
16. Fellowship is more than looking at the back of christian heads for an hour in a church building
17. Training children for the Lord requires intentionality, and serious planning--McDonalds, Nikes, Levis, a house, and little league is not parenting...
18. We sing hymns for enjoyment---and so will you (We can choose what we want ourselves to enjoy)
19. God is good, and worthy of praise when things seem great, and when things seem bad. God still loves us and cares for us when it seems like our world has crashed around us
20. Count your blessings, not your troubles
21. Troubles are the tools that God uses to train us for His purpose
22. Learn how to fail successfully--failure can be more valuable than winning sometimes
23. Learn how to sympathize
24. Learn how to use interruptions for Good--who knows but that

the interruption was God's plan for you today

25. Enjoy, and Praise God for the beauty of His Nature
26. Learn to Yield, Submit, and Surrender--it is strength not weakness (Jesus our example submitted to sinful men)
27. Learn to be Humble--Pride goes before a fall, and God resists proud people--He gives grace to the Humble
28. Take care of your body--it is God's temple...exercise, eat right, get plenty of sleep...
29. Learn self discipline...start with your mind and your mouth ...if a man can control his tongue, he can control his whole body
30. Ask for Help...Weak people are too proud to ask...everyone can benefit by asking
31. Love your enemies--do good to those who mistreat you--it is God's way, and it gets rid of enemies by making them friends
32. Treat other people the way you want to be treated--not the way they deserve--Jesus said so
33. Do twice as much as you have to--more than you are required double your duty--Jesus commanded it
34. Do not give first rate priority to second rate causes (Not with your thoughts, time, or money)
35. Do not resist evil people--yield to them--let them win-- let them sue you, let them slap your other cheek, go the second mile, let them borrow---Jesus
36. Happiness is a choice. Be content with God's love when you have nothing else. This life is very short--it is just a test to see where you will spend eternity
37. Listen to advice and accept instruction--Fools say, "you can't tell me what to do"
38. Resist the Devil and he will run from you--run from anything that even hints of evil--Satan and Hell are real and many will find the easy way to destruction
39. Practice Spiritual Warfare--Our fight is not against flesh and blood
40. Choose to rule your feelings with your will--it is a lie to believe

you can't help what you feel, think, or want

41. Don't worry about basic needs for life--Just try to serve God first, and He will make sure you have food and clothes
42. Be patient--God isn't on our timetable--He wants to work in us
43. Choose a job that will best allow you to serve God first-- serving God is our real purpose on earth--not making a living
44. This world is not our home--we're just camping out here-- don't get too comfortable
45. Don't collect nice stuff for yourself on earth--collect stuff for yourself in heaven
46. Don't focus on yourself--act like the dead person you claim to be
47. Learn to say you are sorry, admit wrong, confess your faults get things right now--don't sleep on it---GO NOW
48. Be gentle--never be rough and harsh with your words or actions
49. Love Lost People--Long for them--God does
50. Be Faithful--Do what you said you would--follow through

Dr. Joe Brumfield Sept 16, 2001

Why Some Kids Leave Church

Problem: 45% leave the church after High School   (Lewis, Dodd, Tippins...)
                12 1/2 % of these return after they get married and have kids

Bible Principles: Deut 6:4-9; Eph 6:1-4; Pro 19:18; Pro 4:23; Pro 29:21

Some Kids leave the Church because:

1. Their parents did not model real Christianity--they just taught it
2. They know the truth, but choose the wages of sin--sin is fun for a short time
3. They fall into temptation and are trapped by their own sinful desires
4. They perceive the Church as being hypocritical, cold, legalistic, or unloving
5. They are so desperate to be accepted that they join with bad companions
6. They are negatively influenced by non-spiritual media influence
7. Their parents are too busy making a living to share a life
8. They don't feel valued and needed by the church
9. Many people expect them to be worthless--negative prophecy
10. They can't tell that Christianity really does anything for them
11. They feel that God has let them down
12. They believe that they have gone too far to return home to God
13. They have some sinful habit that they can't seem to beat
14. They are overwhelmed by guilt from something in the past
15. They were sexually or emotionally wounded in the past and can't fit God
        into that painful worldview
16. They don't feel loved, wanted, and accepted by the church
17. Christianity seems boring to them
18. They think that God wants to hinder them from enjoyable things
19. Their parents gave the influence time away to schools, coaches, little league,
20. They think they will come to God later--plenty of time
21. They are swayed by unspiritual companions
22. They buy the teachings/love/value of false religions
23. They buy the world view that everyone sincere will go to heaven
24. They think the Church is "judging" everyone and is therefore unloving
25. They are trained by hours of negative influence
26. Their only spiritual training is in the Church building
27. Their parents are pew sitters and not actively involved in Kingdom work
28. They were not disciplined lovingly when young
29. Their parents do not discipline like they said they would--God won't either
30. They are allowed to date and marry persons who are negative influences
31. Their parents are too permissive: let kids do pretty much what they want-
        kids grow up thinking God is also permissive: most anything goes
32. Their parents don't cultivate a relationship when kids are young---therefore
        they don't have a relationship when kids are older
33. They see their parents watching trash on TV, listening to trash music--

Joe Brumfield 3-2-03
Revised 1-16-05

War Games: Practice Scenarios To Set up Family Defenses

Prepare In Advance For These Frequently Successful Attacks against Christians (Reasons Christians Often Fall):

1. They aren't in love with Jesus.

2. They are in love with the world.

3. Christianity doesn't seem to work for them.

4. Christianity seems boring.

5. They do not understand how much God love's them.

6.   Eternal things do not seem urgent right now.

7. Following Jesus is not popular.

8. Christianity doesn't seem to answer the problems and questions that they have.

9. They do not know what is at stake.

10. They do not perceive the reality of the unseen world.

11.   Media influence and worship

12.   Poor role modeling from parents

13.   Not feeling a part--not owning the church

14.   Kids don't perceive parents faith as genuine

15.   Parents seem to be trying to earn way to heaven

Truths about Jesus that give confidence to struggling believers (Teaching answers for Satan's Attacks):

1. He knows how we feel---he has been there –tempted in every way like you
2. He loves us more than we know—even when we fail

3. Jesus wants us to be saved!   Doesn't want anyone to perish

4. He paid the full price for our sin---took it—gave us his righteousness
5. He lives to intercede for you!!

6. No temptation will be too strong---way of escape guaranteed

7. Everyone who wants to live a Godly life in Jesus will be persecuted

8. Seek God and you will find...   Hunger for Righteousness—Will be filled
9. Forgives our sins and remembers them no more

10. Lives in us through the Holy Spirit
11. We are family---not ashamed to call us brothers!
12. He rose from the dead—went to heaven---prepared a place for us
13. He is waiting for the day set...coming to get us—his bride
14. Jesus is interceding for Christians right Now!!
15. "Do Not Fear" perhaps the most oft repeated encouragement in scripture

Ten most important things a teen needs to learn about Christianity: (Joe Brumfield's feeble ideas (7-20-99)

1. Jesus loves them unconditionally--whether they are good or bad.
2. The things of the world are only temporary givers of fulfillment--only God gives true joy.
3. Christianity will work for you--but often not in the ways you expect--God's ways are not our ways.
4. People who are bored with Christianity don't understand what it is all about---it is exciting, challenging, dangerous and fulfilling
5. Eternal things are urgent, and earthly things that seem urgent, may be unimportant
6. Following Jesus will not be popular, but only wimps have to constantly please others to like themselves
7. Christ has an answer to every problem you have. God doesn't promise to get rid of your problems, but to help you through them while leaning on Him.
8. There are many truths from God that are unchanging. Truth doesn't change. Only those who truly love truth will make it!
9. Most people will be lost, and few will find the narrow path to life. One must do God's will, and not their own
10. The unseen world is real. Satan is after you, and has specific traps set to catch you. We are in a battle, and there is no middle ground--you are on one side or the or the other!

Sample Letter to Grown Adult Children

1. It is hard for me to come talk to you about these things because:

2. Although it is easy for me to blame my upbringing or _____ circumstances, I take responsibility for...

3. I wish that I had shown you more love by...

4. I'm sorry that I treated your mom/dad...

5. One thing I really wish that I had done more with you is...

6. I wish that I could take back...

7. I know that I hurt God and I hurt you when I ...

8. I have been praying that God would...

9. I am so ashamed that...

10. What could I do so that you would forgive all of the hurts and wrongs that I have caused against you?

11. Will you please pray that God will...

12. I want us to start a new chapter in our relationship by...

13. I love you so much that...

14. I will love you forever because...

15. My greatest joy will be to see you in heaven because...

16. Please pray for me that God will...

Dr. Joe Brumfield, Sept 2000

THE MOST IMPORTANT LESSONS TO TEACH YOUR CHILDREN

Dr. Brumfield

1. HOW TO TREAT A SPOUSE

2. HOW TO FORGIVE SELF AND OTHERS

3. HOW TO HAVE A THANKFUL SPIRIT

4. THAT PARENTS DISAGREE AND FIGHT BUT STILL LOVE EACH OTHER

5. HOW TO RESOLVE PROBLEMS

6. HOW TO SUPPORT YOUR SPOUSE IN HARD TIMES

7. HOW TO BE COMMITTED EVEN WHEN YOU DON'T FEEL LIKE IT

8. HOW TO COMPLIMENT RATHER THAN CRITICIZE

9. HOW TO PRAY

10. HOW TO ADMIT WHEN YOU ARE WRONG

11. THAT HAPPINESS COMES FROM INSIDE, NOT THROUGH THINGS

12. HOW TO SUBMIT TO AUTHORITY

13. HOW TO OVERLOOK SOMEONE'S FAULTS

14. HOW TO SEEK TRUTH AND NOT BELIEVE THE DEVIL'S LIES

77

FAMILY RULES

1. Do not eat with the television on.
2. We do not say, "Shut up" or "Stupid."
3. Bedtime: Hug, kiss, and say, "I love you."
4. Cannot go to bed until fights are solved.
5. Stay at the table till everyone is done.
6. Ask to be excused -- compliment the cook.
7. No television or play until homework and chores are done.
8. Prayers and Bible reading, and brush before bed and after breakfast.
9. Pray with and for your children.
10. Pray before eating.
11. No sweets before meals; no dessert if you did not eat your supper.
12. No ball-playing inside the house.
13. You must tell parents in advance who you are with and where you are. Parents must approve of friends before activities together.
14. Clothes complaints? Wash them yourself / Modesty
15. Place your dirty clothes *in* the hamper.
16. Rinse dishes off before loading dishwasher.
17. We will have a family devotional every day.
18. If you have something good to say, say it -- otherwise, do not say it.
19. No sass, smart talk, or "backtalk."
20. Sing in Church -- we like it.
21. We don't whine or gripe.
22. Everybody works while anybody works.
23. We always go to church meetings.
24. If you get it out, put it up.
25. Eating and driving are special times for family encouragement.
26. Share your feelings -- rather than pouting.
27. If Mom says no -- Dad does too!
28. We speak with a gentle tone.

-- Consistent Anchors in Life: Things I can count on

* The clearer the Family Rules, the higher the self-esteem.

Changes Needed in Dads:

1. More face to face time! One parent with one child. No technology. Fishing, camping, hunting, etc. No distractions! "Give me the number one spot for attention for a little while."

2. Confession and Honesty! " Dad, tell me the mistakes you've made so I won't make them. Pretending you are/were perfect decreases your modeling value. It does not make me respect you more!"

3. "Dad, It feels like you love me IF I make the team or get great grades. I long for you to love me for who I am, not for what I can accomplish that makes YOU look good."

4. "Dad, you talk about politics, the economy, the weather, and sports in public! I need to see your boldness talking about Jesus!"

5. I wish it felt safe and comfortable to share my real struggles with my dad.

6. "Dad, quit zoning out with the TV! Talk and share your feelings with me."

7. "Dad, If you really care more about spiritual things than your job, show it!"

8. "Dad, did/do you struggle with lust and masturbation? Did you have sex before marriage? Did you try alcohol or smoke pot? If you won't be transparent, don't expect it from me."

9. "Dad, please listen to my opinions before you make up your mind. Sometimes I feel like you listen, but it makes absolutely no difference in your conclusions. This means you didn't really listen."

10. I wish my dad had more confidence in my decisions, and in God taking care of me.

11. I wish my dad would get control of his anger.

The Research of Brumfield as well as that of Lewis, Dodd, and Tippins reveals some top desires of several thousand teens for their parents. When so many teens see the same changes needed in parents, the need for change is urgent.

Changes Needed in Moms:

1. "Mom, you have to let me grow up! Let God take care of me and quit worrying so much." Trust God a little more. He loves me too!

2. My mother needs to exercise more, eat better, and get more rest so she will have time and energy left for me. She needs to quit doing so much stuff.

3. I wish my mom would tell me about her dating days, and be really honest.

4. My mother needs to gradually work herself out of a job....gradually reduce her rules so I can actually grow up. I have to think for myself, and my mom needs to let go, and put her relationship with dad first!

5. I need my mom to value my friends because I care about them, and not measure them by their clothes and their music.

6. I wish it felt that my mother valued what I think over what other people think. Is my opinion not more trustworthy than other adults?

7. My mother is so cranky at "that time of the month." She needs to get a handle on it, and choose to be nice anyway!

8. My mom needs to be more romantic with my dad. I need to see her chasing him romantically so I have something to look forward to when I get married. If mom and dad don't keep it "hot at home" why should I wait for marriage?

9. I wish my mom understood that despising my music is like despising me. It is part of who I am.

10. I need my mom to have confidence in me and trust me. She needs to explain that she looks under my bed and through my stuff because she loves me and she knows that Satan tempts really good people.

78c

ABOVE ALL ELSE GUARD YOUR HEART
Proverbs 4:23

Eph 6:4 Fathers don't
Exasperate your
kids

Heb 4:12...The
Word judges the
thoughts and

What was in the hearts of kids who shot their classmates?

Shooter Profile: White, middle class, male---slightly dysfunctional in rel w/dad

Columbia Univ Study: Relationship with Dad predicts problems more than
family structure: Single parent kids= 30% more likely to use drugs/ alcohol,
 Intact family w/ fair to poor rel w/dad=68% more likely to use drugs/alcohol
Intact family with good to excellent rel w/dad= 94% less likely to use
drugs/alcohol

1. Your heart predicts your eternity. Your heart is you!
2. As a man thinks in his heart—so is he
3. What ever a man sows—that will he also reap
4. We will be judged by every idle word
5. Sow a thought, Reap an action, Sow an action, Reap a Habit, Sow
   A Habit, Reap a Lifestyle, Sow a Lifestyle, Reap an Eternity
6. There are no events, words, songs, movies, etc. that have no effect
   on a person. Everything that you see and hear becomes a part of
   you and changes your heart and life in the future.
7. Everything that goes into your heart will come out as a thought,
   word, or action.
8. A Parents main jobs are to stop negative input into the hearts of
   their children, and to increase the output of positive input.
9. Leaving the Radio, Internet, Television, etc. going unplanned and
   Unfiltered may be one of the most dangerous mistakes made by
   parents.
10. Why not have kids drink out or the toilet instead of leaving an un-
    Guarded stream of media flowing into their hearts. Which is
    worse—Physical sickness and death or spiritual sickness and
    death? Should one fear the death of the body or of the soul?

Dr. Joe Brumfield

MOST IMPORTANT THINGS FOR MOTHERS

1. Love God with all your heart—your children will see it in your actions
2. Talk about God and His love all day—instead of house decorating, Social issues, politics, or local gossip
3. Model a gentle and quiet spirit –win hearts and arguments with kindness not with words
4. Serve quietly out of love for God –little eyes are watching
5. Work on your inner beauty before your clothes, your figure, your hairstyle, and your tan.
6. Sing lots of praise to God while you work (this is your work)\
7. Understand that your primary value is not cooking, cleaning, and laundry, but meeting the spiritual and emotional needs of your family.
8. Put your husband before your kids—for your kids sake
9. Learn the incredible power of submission—your kids will see Jesus!
10. Teach a love for God's Word with intentionality, rather than with mere Sunday school attendance
10. Model parent problem resolution by winning without a word by loving attitude and lifestyle.
11. Put loving words at the dinner table ahead of the physical nutrition on the table.
12. Give priority to lots of hugs and kisses for your husband and kids over ironing all their clothes and doing their laundry! Their emotional health is more important. Teach them to help with the laundry and ironing.

A mother's value is in being the loving warm emotional hub of the family, and not primarily in cooking, cleaning, and washing clothes!
Dr. Joe Brumfield

How To Get Your Teenager To Talk To You
(And Other Important things to do for your teen)
By Dr. Joe Brumfield, February 11, 1999

1. Spend lots of time with them (Deut. 6)
2. Speak with actions rather than mere words
3. Give lots of appropriate touching: back scratches, foot rubs, hugs, arms around the shoulder
4. Make self vulnerable and approachable by
   a. confessing personal faults
   b. asking for advice
   c. asking for their opinion
5. Start the talking/habit when they are very young-- don't wait till they are teens
6. Pray with them constantly
7. Know about their life: their friends, hobbies, sports, music, nicknames, school frustrations, fears, anxieties, favorite clothes, etc.
8. Accept them and love them no matter what--they will test your unconditional love. This does not mean you have to accept bad things they do. Separate the sin from the sinner.
9. Speak nicely about their friends. Be nice to their friends. Help them associate with others who will encourage them. Invite these "good" friends over so you can facilitate valuable fun times
10. Give your teens lots of honest praise. It must be genuine and deserved.

11. Take your teen on special outings at every opportunity. Make it happen! You will not have this chance much longer. Give them total attention. Let them know often how important they are to you. Take daughters on dates. Take sons hunting and fishing (daughters also) The goal is not to hunt or fish or play, but to show them how much you value them. Make them feel important. They are!

12. Get your teen away from everyone and everything else. Just you and them together. Only after you have spent lots of time together can a teen open up and begin sharing their true self and their true feelings.

13. Listen to your teen when they do talk. Stop what you are doing, and give them full attention. Make them know that what they say means something to you.

14. Work on your marriage for their security sake. The more they see how your marriage is secure, the more secure they will feel. They more they see how much you enjoy your marriage, the more they will be able to build a good one of their own some day.

15. Parents must stay parents, and not slip into the buddy role. Many parents cannot get back into the authority role where kids desperately need them to be.

16. Give clear rules so they know where they stand. Let your yes be yes, and your no be no... Explain the rules carefully, and have them repeat them back to you.

17. Listen to their music with them. Learn to appreciate what is good. Teach them to discriminate themselves.

18. Communicate to them that there will always be a place for them with you. Teens top fears include the fear of having to grow up and leave home.

19. Teach the teen to ask for attention when they need it. Start when they can talk.

20. Stick with the rules you give them. Do not allow them to manipulate you or they will grow up to be manipulators. Common Cons by Barbara Coloroso
    a. Con #1: Getting parents to change their mind/decision by pressuring you-- begging, promising, crying, and yelling

    b. Con#2: Arguing: none of my friends have to, its not fair, this is dumb, you are mean... Don't be lured into arguing with your kids.

    c. Con #3: total rebellion: "you can't make me--spank me--it won't hurt--I'll run away" Sulk and pout

21. Never make threats that you aren't willing to carry out. It will show up in their communication.

22. Refuse to argue with your kids--you will lose.

23. Do not take back responsibility that you have given to

them. Tell them, have them repeat it, and then follow through with the consequences. Inconsistent parents produce inconsistent teens.

24. Model Fair fighting (arguments) when necessary, and be sure they see how to admit wrong, apologize, and how to ask for forgiveness. They will learn to resolve problems by watching you!! Anyone want to play cold war??

25. Give them responsibilities that fit their age. Let these responsibilities continue to grow as their age and maturity permit: cleaning room, sweeping, ironing, cooking, washing dishes, doing laundry, paying bills, reconciling a checkbook, buying their own clothes, managing a savings account... Teach them to think for themselves while they are still at home where you can observe and correct. Don't cripple them by doing everything for them.

26. Teach them how to resolve problems and how to talk things out. Require them to manage/control their emotions. Teach them that happiness is a choice. So is anger, love, etc. Teach them to share their feelings while they are very young--then it won't be like pulling teeth when they are old.

27. Teach kids how to work. Don't pay them for everything that they do. They are part of the family. You will give them value this way. Many teens know that they are a financial liability by listing to, "do you know how much you are costing me...?"

28. Allow kids to feel the consequences of their own actions. Don't constantly rescue them from their mistakes. Just love them through. Make them own their own problems.

29. Don't provoke your children. Griping, yelling, and nagging are not productive. Be swift to hear, slow to speak, and slow to wrath.

Interesting Facts about teens:
   sources: Lewis, Dodd, Tippins
1. They are desperate for security and unconditional love.
2. The fear of having to grow up and leave home is likely at the heart of many teen problems.
3. Many of their pranks and problems stem from their conscious or unconscious attempts to get attention and recognition. (Especially from their fathers)
4. Many teen guys give affection to get sex. Many teen girls give sex to get the affection missing from their father.
5. Daughters with a very close loving relationship with a father who spends lots of time with them are much less vulnerable to sexual activity before marriage.
6. Sons who have a close loving relationship with a father who spends lots of time, talk, and non-sexual touch with

them--are less vulnerable to homosexual tendencies.

7. Kids who are pressured and pushed by rigid boundries and authoritarian parents who show little affection, seem more likely to become sexually active.

8. The more time kids spend with direct loving attention from parents, the less likely they are to use alcohol or drugs.

9. Christian teens tend to have a higher technical virginity rate than non-christian kids. They tend to have a higher rate of oral sex and mutual masturbation. (They seem to be thinking, "At least we didn't _do it!_")

10. Christian teens tend to have a lower rate of illegal drug use than non-christian kids. They seem to use more legal drugs: diet pills, sleeping pills, mom's Rx for ____ Some Christian teens have been taught not to break the letter of the law, but they don't seem to understand the heart of the law very well.

11. The major motivations teens have for avoiding alcohol and drugs are:
    -fear of disappointing God
    -respect for self
    -parent disapproval
    -reputation
    -other ways to cope
    -they refuse the control of peers
    -fear of the unknown
    -don't like the taste

Wise parents should build on these motivations!!

12. Common motivations of some teens to use alcohol
    and drugs:
    -popularity
    -pleasure
    -boredom
    -low self esteem
    -get power over my life
    -gain attention

13. Kids who attend regular youth church activities are
    12 times <u>less</u> likely to drink alcohol.

14. Teen communication is often the opposite of what the
    words say:
    -kids who say no mean "please say no to me"
    - "I don't need you" means "I need you desperately"
    - "It's no big deal" means "It means everything"
    - "I don't need rules" means "I long for rules"

15. Train up a child in the way he should go, and try
    walking in it yourself sometime. Teens seem to hear
    modeling communication much more clearly than they
    hear verbal communication.

16. Parental neglect may be the very worst kind of abuse
    Physical abuse cuts and bruises heal up in time.
    Emotional abuse may not.

17. The teen female from a single parent family is the most
    at risk sexually

Parenting Tips

That turned out Good Christians--Brumfield 96/97

Christian Students Report on things their parents did that really helped. Consider the following:

1. Read to children
2. Sense of humor (ability to laugh)
3. Always be honest with kids
4. Dad wrestled with me
5. Pick their fleas
6. Camping
7. Christian Camps
8. Mission trips
9. Mom let us help with the dishes and fold the towels even though it took twice as long
10. Dad waited for us at the bus stop -- he checked our clothes etc.
11. Long family bike rides -- we talked as we rode
12. King size bed -- we all gathered there to rest, joke, and talk
13. My parents came to all my activities/games
14. My parents gave me jobs to earn money for the things I wanted (sometimes they even made up jobs)
15. My dad clearly explained what I did wrong and how it affected things
16. My parents gave me options and taught me independence
17. My dad hugged me and let me cry on his shoulder
18. After every evening meal we would rush to sit on our parents laps and talk
19. Every night everyone had to sit together for supper
    and talk -- no TV or radio, other things were canceled
20. My dad and brother went canoeing and fishing
21. Mom let me pick seeds and we gardened together and talked while we worked
22. Dad paid real close attention to us when we talked -- I knew he could tell if I lied, so I told the truth
23. After he whopped "the fire" out of me he told me that he loved me, only then would I break the tough act and cry
24. Mom had snacks ready when we came home from school -- we sat and talked and did our homework together
25. Every Sunday after church services Mom asked us how we could apply the lesson at school and home
26. Whenever we had a question they carefully explained it -- they never gave us a "pat" answer
27. Every Saturday my dad took me (his girl) to breakfast -- nobody else took their kids
28. Mom traveled -- Dad helped us make a cake for her before she returned
29. My parents learned to be both my parents and my friends, so I would talk to them
30. My dad shared his feelings with me, so I was encouraged to share my feelings with him
31. Dad took us shopping for mom's gift -- he said my part was $.25 and I felt like I helped pay
32. My mom put little notes in my lunch box like; "smile"-- that is why I always smile now; "I am thinking about you, I am praying for you"
33. My parents did not push me into anything but supported me full force when I chose
34. My dad always played on my team when my friends came over -- we were best friends
35. My mom, though dying with cancer, never raised her voice... showed us strength in adversity... gave me faith that I now have
36. They always had busy schedules, but when someone needed help -- they made time
37. Mom encouraged me to seek truth for myself but always offered to sit and discuss
38. My dad went on walks with me and always stopped to point out neat rocks and things that no one else would notice
39. When I was home, my dad put off his work and did things with me
40. My parents always encouraged my creative and imaginative side
41. My mom listened and was empathetic; she did not correct every little mistake

Parenting Tips

That turned out Good Christians--Brumfield 96/97

42. My parents told me about mistakes they had made--now I feel comfortable sharing mine.
43. Tho I had 3 brothers, my dad played one-on-one with me (his daughter) and made sure I was not left out
44. My parents made me fight thru some situations myself -- taught me that life is not fair
45. My dad bought little things and stuck them under my pillow
46. Dad told me "I am more in love with your mother than when I married her" -- relieved all of my concerns about divorce
47. Hospitality... I cannot remember a time when someone extra did not live at my house
48. My dad gave secret gifts to those in need
49. My mom sent letters and said that she missed me
50. Our family went on Saturday and cleaned the church building -- gave us a sense of ownership and belonging to the church -- we played "Samuel"
51. My mom bought clothes and groceries and left them on the doorsteps of Christians in need
52. Every night my dad knelt by my bed and we prayed together
53. I still feel comfortable calling my dad "Daddy"
54. My parents respected me (even when I was little), it taught me to respect others
55. My mom always told me "remember who you are"   My dad always tells me "I love you"
56. We took on a needy family at Christmas time -- it has made me more generous... we loved to see their reaction
57. We went camping and took no food, we had to eat the fish we caught
58. Every night at the dinner table they quizzed the kids over their homework
59. Dad asked if we wanted to go cut trees for firewood (we were really to small to help)
60. Dad took his little girls hunting
61. My dad did magic shows for us kids and asked us to help -- at parties we got to assist and he told us the secrets
62. My dad played with kids -- they thought he was great -- I got esteem from that
63. We cleaned the furniture and played pillow football on our knees
64. My parents never seemed to have a conversation without bringing God or spiritual things into it
65. My parents stayed together almost 50 years before my mom died -- I have heard that 90% of the couples who have a family devotional never divorce -- it worked

ADVICE FOR FUTURE FAMILIES

Brumfield 95/96

-- Regulate TV and movie watching of kids
-- Pray while on a date
-- Have a regular family devotional time
-- When you are mad, work it out now rather than later
-- Do not discipline a child when you are angry
-- Find out what bugs your girlfriend/fiancee before you marry her
-- Communicate with statements like "One thing that I want from you but am afraid to ask for is..." and "One
      reason I make it hard for you to do this is..."
-- Eat together with family
-- Praise kids for their accomplishments
-- Be willing to apologize and be humbled before your children
-- Clip coupons for the store; and keep the amount saved by using coupons for special purpose
-- Always respect your spouse's job: do not play salary games
-- Do not let a job come between you and your kids
-- Always hug the kids and tell them that you love them
-- Find our spouse's tendencies toward anger before you marry
-- Put God first: but do not neglect wife and children for Him
-- Do not forget that "doing things for God" includes loving family
-- Parents complement family members in front of other people
-- Let each child be an individual
-- Choose your battles: do not make a big fuss over small issues
-- Have relationship right with God before trying to have a deep relationship with someone else
-- Do not gullibly assume your kids are perfect
-- Do not split up: give God the authority
-- Make a list of traits you want your ideal spouse to have: then instead of looking for that person, become
      that person
-- Let your kid help even if his help is actually a hindrance, in order to give him a sense of self-worth
-- Be unified in decisions with kids (do not allow the "If Dad says no, ask Mom" syndrome)
-- Have a list of things you want to do in a jar; pull one out every so often
-- Do not have the "good guy" parent and the "bad guy" parent
-- Reserve some time just for self and spouse, away from kids; and do not forget about the romantic love
      aspect of marriage
-- Do not contradict spouse directly in front of kids; talk about it before or after
-- Take time out, a weekend or whatever, to talk about sex with kids
-- Do not make children afraid of sex or make them think it is dirty; but do teach that sex outside of marriage
      is sinful
-- Do not talk negatively about your spouse; it will make your kids insecure
-- Ask for suggestions from your kids in solving problems
-- Do not compare your kids with each other
-- Do a daily review with your kids
-- Ask kids how they think they should be punished (but don't always go with their suggestions, of course!)
-- Dress up for spouse; do not dress up for other people while being sloppy around spouse
-- Do not let your relationship with your spouse replace your relationship with God; and do not try to get
      from your spouse what only God can give
-- Have family vacations at a motel with no TV
-- Have family traditions and "rituals"
-- Tell your kids to "work it out together" or have parents mediate without controlling

HOW TO RAISE CHILDREN WHO WILL DIVORCE THEIR SPOUSE WHEN THEY GROW UP

The truth is they never grew up--and we made sure they wouldn't. They are just large children who are waiting for us to bring their bottle, or whatever they <u>feel</u> will make them happy!

What Defect do People have before they marry that encourages Divorce later?
1. The idea that marriage will make them happy
2. The idea that their spouse will meet all their needs
3. The idea that if they aren't happy, it is because the spouse is failing to do the things that would make them happy.

What Truths Must Be Taught To Teens
1. Happiness comes from inside
2. People and things can't make you happy
3. Until you let go the idea that a spouse is what makes you happy, or unhappy, YOU WILL NEVER BE HAPPY!
4. It is easier to blame our discontent and lack of fulfillment, and failure to be happy on our spouse because:
    a. It takes the blame off of us!
    b. IF it were our fault we would have to do lots of Uncomfortable things:
        1) Admit we are wrong
        2) Swallow our pride
        3) Grow and change which are uncomfortable
        4) Work, Sweat, and Toil at building the marriage

    c. Excuses that sound like reasons are comfortable and easy! Joe Brumfield, May 21, 1999

91

Divorce Proofing Your Children
20 Years In Advance

1. Put spiritual values first
2. Avoid the effects of pampering
3. Teach Internal Locus of Control
4. Debunk the Devil's favorite myths and lies
5. Teach selflessness and self control
6. Foster "real" expectations for marriage
7. Say "No!" and mean it
8. Watch for the danger of too much choice
9. Practice giving unconditional love
10. Have a "fantastic" love life; model incredible romance
11. Help kids get their self esteem: from God not men
12. Fill their emotional love tank
13. Show them how to fight in a way that resolves problems.
14. Model forgiveness and forgetfulness "Sewer Control"
15. Give first rate priorities to first rate things!
16. Watch out for "worshiping work; playing at worship, and working at play"
17. Teach God's plan for marriage, and his "hate" for divorce
18. Model great communication skills:
    "One thing I need from you..."
    "On a scale of one to ten..."
    "What makes you feel loved by me..."
19. Help them learn good money management when they are young: giving, saving, and the use of credit
20. Model "time control" with family priorities in mind
21. Put your spouse before your children so they will
22. Pray constantly with them regarding their marriages

Dr. Joe S. Brumfield Nov 19, 1997

PROACTIVE INTENTIONAL CHILD TRAINING
By Dr. Joe Brumfield

Number the following life lessons (in order of importance to you) that you want to make sure to teach your kids before you die:

_____how to mow the grass
_____how to do math
_____how to gripe about the government
_____how to love a spouse who seems almost unlovable
_____how to write
_____how to love and praise God even when you don't understand why things happen
_____how to bat, catch, and throw a baseball
_____how to forgive yourself and other people
_____how to love those who don't like you
_____how to tackle a runner
_____how to be honest
_____how to balance a checkbook
_____how to cultivate a personal relationship with God
_____how to drive
_____how to pray
_____how to fish
_____how to go the second mile
_____how to change the oil
_____how to resolve marriage conflict
_____how to do laundry
_____how to be patient and gentle
_____how to manage money
_____how to say your sorry
_____how to survive emotionally, spiritually and physically
_____how to pretend
_____how to know that if nobody else loves you---God does
_____the lie that Strong people don't need counseling or help
_____how to be Humble rather than Proud

PROACTIVE INTENTIONAL CHILD TRAINING cont.
By Dr. Joe Brumfield

Number the following life lessons (in order of importance to you) that you want to teach (are teaching) your kids before you die:

____Value of material things: We don't say if you are rich you'll be popular, but we all notice the in style clothes, and the cars...

____Social values: Nice cars get immediate results

____Temporary versus eternal: Being good only pays off when you die!!

____Respect of Persons: give gifts to your teacher--not the custodian???

____say "yes sir" to the coach, not to _____

____how to work hard

____how to speak critically of others

____how to iron clothes

____how to use the computer

____How to admit when you are wrong

____How to submit to authority

____How to plant a garden

____How to overlook someone's faults

____How to be content with little or much

____How to entertain yourself

____How to be thankful for everything

____How to romance a husband or wife

____How to hold a grudge

____How to pout

____How to putt

____How to give service

____How to serve us

____How to choose happiness

____that "I can't help the way I feel"

____How to build a house

____How to build a home

Love Killers

1. Constant Criticism
2. Rare Praise or None
3. Unmet Emotional Needs
4. Unhealthy Family Baggage
5. Job Failures
6. Personal Dissatisfaction
7. Spiritual Failures.
8. Unresolved Guilt Feelings
9. Returning Evil For Evil
10. Failure to Reveal Hurts
11. Refusal to Deal With Problems
12. Power Struggles
13. Lack of Future Mutual Goals
14. Selfish Actions.
15. Resentment and Jealousy of Spouse
16. Over-activity: Busy with Earthly Cares
17. Requiring Spouse to Meet all of Your Emotional Needs
18. Comparisons (depression, here I come)
19. Feeling Left Out or Neglected
20. Anger - trying to punish others or self

Dr. Joe Brumfield
Harding University

Divorce Effects Conclusions from Researcher
E. Mavis Hetherington

30 yr longitudinal study on the effects of Divorce
bk: <u>For better or for worse: Divorce reconsidered</u>

25 % of kids from divorced homes end up with some
kind of psychological-emotional-social problems as
compared with 10% from a non-divorced families

Much may be from a self fulfilling prophecy--you will
have a messed up future because your parents divorced.
She suggests that it often doesn't manifest itself all of
the time.

Divorce is more a symptom of the problem and not the
root problem—has to do with parents getting along

Kids who have problems before the divorce knock the
numbers down to only 2/3 of the 25 % (In other words,
The divorce pretty much caused these problems)

Researcher J. Wallerstein sees more problems in
Most of the children of divorce, and suggests that
The problems follow the children into adulthood.

Wallerstein followed a smaller group for 20-30 years,
but did in depth interviews, while Hetherington
followed a bigger group without such in depth work.

Parents with Misbehaving Teens
Areas to Question:

1. Closeness of relationship between family members:
   -especially check closeness with father
2. Check to see what child is gaining from misbehavior that they are not receiving at home
3. What might be happening in the home that could make child feel lack of security?
4. Check the parents marriage (Children feel great stress, and tend to exhibit symptoms when they see or feel stress between their parents)
5. Check the Parents sexual relationship. (When parents do not feel close to each other, kids often feel insecure)
6. What is being discussed at home that makes the child fear the future?
7. How positive is the communication between all family members
8. When was the Home a safe and encouraging environment--when everyone wanted to be there, or when was it a place of criticism and argument where everyone tended to avoid being there?
9. About How many positive strokes do mom and dad give to each other daily compared to the number of negative strokes they give? (This gives the marital health indication)
   5 positive to 1 negative is a great relationship! When the ratio gets as low as one negative message for every positive message the prediction is relationship failure within 1-2 years.
10. What is the positive to negative message ratio between parent and child?
11. What have been some of the major family stressors in the recent past? (Deaths, Illnesses, Finances, Sexual abuse, drug use, problems with relatives, job problems, parent fighting, divorce, problems at school, grades, ...)

Kids: What Predicts That They Will Stay Faithful? 2-28-03
By Dr. Joe Brumfield

Flavil Yeakley reminded me this morning of a Study published in ACU's Youth Ministry Bulletin around 1985:

After High School, Kids stay faithful (continue attending):

20% of the time if parents attended Church but weren't actively involved

40% of the time if parents attended and the parent of the opposite gender was actively involved

60% of the time if parents attended and the parent of the same gender was actively involved in Church Work
   *note avg 50% retention if only one parent involved

80-90% of the time if both parents attended and were actively involved in church work

Kids curriculum was not predictive? But if parents seemed to be actively challenged in the Bible School Curriculum, the percentage of faithful kids in those congregations was higher.

Another study (maybe Lewis, Dodd, and Tippins) shows that we lose 45% of our young people (they leave the church) after High School graduation. Flavil's study suggests that 12 ½ % of these return to the church after they get married and have kids. (net loss then would only be 32 ½ %)

Flavil said the fact that 90% of kids who attend state universities leave the church is misleading. They quit because they weren't faithful when they arrived at college, not because the "wicked" college destroyed their faith. It is the home/family spiritual training that is predictive. A "pagan" school doesn't try to rescue kids who are spiritually weak or dead. A Christian school at least tries. You might do all right if you send kids who are very spiritually strong to a State University. If kids are not spiritually strong, they might make it at a Christian University. Neither school is a guarantee of spiritual success or failure.

Parenting Styles and How Your Kids are Likely to Turn Out:

Researchers have uncovered links between parenting styles, and how children turn out in later life. Psychologist Diana Baumrind conducted a study on more than 100 preschool-age children (Baumrind, 1967, 1991) She identified three different parent styles, and Maccoby and Martin added a fourth style in 1983.

These four parenting styles are

1. **Authoritarian**- strict rules with little or no explanation, punishment, high demands, and little responsiveness to children.
2. **Permissive**- these indulgent parents have few demands and rarely discipline. Parents expect little in the way of self control. These parents are very nurturing, lenient, and usually let the children regulate themselves for the most part. The parents communicate often, and deal with their kids as a buddy or a friend and not as a parent or boss.
3. **Neglectful**- parents are not responsive and have little communication with the child. The parents are very detached and only meet very basic child needs if at all. These kids are sometimes described as "latch-key" kids.
4. **Authoritative**- parents are loving and nurturing, but have clear rules and guidelines and discipline disobedience firmly. Rules are discussed and explained. Parents listen to their children and are responsive. Parents are assertive but not overly restrictive. Discipline is for training instead of merely punitive. Children are taught self-control, cooperation, and self-regulation.

How Parenting Styles Impact Children:

Many studies have been done since Baumrind's early study of 100 preschool children. The results generally show that:

1. **Authoritarian parents** often rear children who do their work well, and follow rules well, but their self esteem, their social skills and their personal happiness are low.
2. **Permissive parents** often have children who are unhappy and have poor self control/self-regulation. These kids don't do as well in school, and they do not deal well with authority. *David Wilmes from the Johnson Institute reports parental permissiveness as a more important risk factor for children using destructive chemicals than even peer pressure.*
3. **Neglectful parents**-are usually linked to the poorest results. The kids are the least competent, have little self-control, and have low self-esteem.
4. **Authoritative parents**- are generally linked to kids who are capable and happy. These kids tend to be more successful then peers raised with a different parenting style. (Maccoby, 1992).

Baumrind, D. (1967). Child-care practices anteceding three patterns of preschool behavior. *Genetic Psychology Monographs, 75,* 43-88.

Baumrind, D. (1991). The influence of parenting style on adolescent competence and substance use. *Journal of Early Adolescence, 11(1),* 56-95.

Blended family from the perspective of the step child:

1. My Identity has been taken away.

2. If one parent abandoned me--I have proof that the other might as well.

3. I'd better fight for my place, or someone may take it away from me.

4. I have lost any security that I had--Everything is up for grabs now--I can count on nothing being the same!

5. If I am kind to my new step-parent, I feel that I am being disloyal to my biological parent that was replaced.

6. I almost feel that I must rebel or resent my present bio parent for what they did to my absent bio parent. Even if I don't feel this way about my new step-parent, my loyalty to my absent parent demands that I stay aloof, keep my distance. I can't let my new step parent be to me anything that my "real" parent was, because I would be betraying my "Lost" parent.

7. For me to accept new things, activities, love, is to say goodby forever to the hope of the old, familiar, whole, unbroken family that I had. "I refuse to let go of my old memories of being loved by two parents Who loved each other."

8. If they try to force me to accept this new reality as "My Family" I will fight to hold on to the old--I will reject it!! They can't take away from me something that is a part of my heart--the old family is a part of me NOT JUST A PART OF THEM!!!

9. I refuse to let my present bio-parent attack my absent bio-parent. I must support my parent who is not here to support themselves.

Joe Brumfield

The Truth about Spanking:

1. God says that children should be disciplined with a rod
Proverbs
Proverbs 22:15
Folly is bound up in the **heart of a child**, but the rod **of** discipline will drive it far **a**way.
Proverbs 13:24
Whoever spares the **rod** hates their **child**ren, but the one who loves their **child**ren is careful to discipline them.
Proverbs 23:13
Saying 13 Do not withhold discipline from a **child**; if you punish them with the **rod**, they will not die.

2. Hebrews says that discipline is painful

3. Hebrews says that if you love your child --you will discipline him

Hebrews 12:7-11 (NIV)

[7] Endure hardship as discipline; God is treating you as his children. For what children are not disciplined by their father? [8] If you are not disciplined—and everyone undergoes discipline—then you are not legitimate, not true sons and daughters at all. [9] Moreover, we have all had human fathers who disciplined us and we respected them for it. How much more should we submit to the Father of spirits and live! [10] They disciplined us for a little while as they thought best; but God disciplines us for our good, in order that we may share in his holiness. [11] No discipline seems pleasant at the time, but painful. Later on, however, it produces a harvest of righteousness and peace for those who have been trained by it.

5. Many wrongly claim that spanking causes kids to hit and to be violent:

ABOUT SPANKING CHILDREN "There's no evidence that a child who is spanked moderately is going to grow up to be a criminal, or antisocial or violent." - S. Kenneth Schonberg, co-chairman, 1996 American Academy of Pediatrics Conference on Corporal Punishment. _U. S. News and World Report_. April 13, 1998.

102

Kids Reject Parent's Religion When They Perceive Hypocrisy

Common Perceptions of Hypocrisy are:

- The Church spends more time planning parties than it spends in prayer meetings
- when we will sit 2 hours for a movie when we can't spend 30 min hearing the word
- Children boss their parents and parents are afraid not to obey
- when people have secret hurts they can't confess because they are afraid that people won't help and forgive—just gossip
- when kids don't feel safe telling their hurts to their parents, and Christians don't feel safe sharing their sins with the Church
- people would rather watch tv with cursing and lying than blessing and singing
- when Christians are so much like their culture that people can't tell the difference
- when people who wouldn't think of walking in darkness don't even flinch at taking a stroll in the shade
- when people will fight for the truth about instrumental music based on the silence of the scripture but they will not love their spouse when the scripture trumpets such commands loudly
- When people spend more time with their kids at sports games than they do with their children in Bible study and prayer
- When parents make kids take vitamins, eat vegetables, and brush their teeth while allowing them to choose any type of music or movie

SPECIFIC SUGGESTIONS FOR CHRISTIAN GRANDPARENTS

Deuteronomy 4:9 Teach it to your children and your Grandchildren...

1. Spiritual Grandparenting must be intentional. Make specific plans!
2. Set clear priorities: Grandparenting over retirement and relaxation
3. Pray for your children, grandchildren, and great grandchildren daily!
4. Say it!!! Modeling alone will not do it!
   a. " I love you—I care more about you getting to heaven than anything" -smile, laugh, and hug them often!
   b. "I made some mistakes in raising your mom/dad"-let them hear you apologizing to their parents for spiritual mistakes, etc. because God resists the proud but gives grace to the humble
   c. "getting to heaven is more important than a good job, house, car..."
   d. "being with the saints is more important than hunting and fishing."
5. Take your grandkids hunting, fishing, camping, etc at every opportunity—make the goal of the conversation spiritual.
6. Show your grandchildren that you are studying, changing, and growing—that it is never too late to improve spiritually
6. Ask your grandchildren to pray for you and their parents—give specific suggestions about what to pray for.
8. Discuss in detail mistakes you made and problems you faced—ask your grandchild for ideas about how he or she might win in these areas when they face them.
9. Write spiritual letters often! It does not have to be long, and spelling and grammar do not matter! They love you, and care about your heart!
10. Discuss your faith at work because......—kids have lots of ideas about what you are ashamed of in public. Is Dad ashamed of God at work?
11. Use your driving time for spiritual learning: Intentional Discussions, Prayer while driving, List spiritual questions, Listen to scripture, Sing hymns together (sing alone if you have to...they will see what you value)
12. Use your work time to invite people to your home for Bible studies...they will see your priorities
13. Have ongoing spiritual discussions at work instead of merely discussion politics, weather, and sports. Jesus said, "If you confess me before men, I will confess you before my Father, but if you do not confess me..."

14. Enjoy being a Christian and let it show.
15. Give them Gifts that cause a use of spiritual time: gift certificate to a Christian Bookstore. Consider what happens when you give them an I-pod, I-pad, smart phone, etc.
16. Ask to listen to "their" music and talk about it.
17. Have discussions often where you practice discerning good from evil.
18. Practice different life scenarios where kids must make choices.
19. Help pay for Christian activities: Christian Camps, mission trips, etc.
20. Ask to see their Bible lessons before you do their school grades—discuss what they learned in Bible Class, or their Bible readings.
21. Give positive strokes for Bible Reading, giving, serving, praying, over positive strokes for worldly accomplishments.
22. Do more clapping, cheering, and inviting friends to their Bible Bowl competition than to their ball games, and school events.
23. Have lots of youth activities at your house! Volunteer to sponsor trips and spiritual activities.
24. Sit by them and their friends at church.
25. Make your home open to them and their friends for fun, snacks, Christian movies and music, Keep a good stock of movies with great spiritual values. Do not allow non spiritual media.
26. Model great treatment of your spouse, and publicly praise them
27. Model hospitality …Kids are learning life priorities.
28. Model faithfulness and caring for spouse. Use kind words only.
29. Model Bible teaching at your family dinner table.
30. Model constant praise. Stroke spiritual qualities not beauty, brains…
31. Model sending cards and making calls: a personal touch.
32. Model helping your wife with the dishes, housework, laundry, etc.
33. Model training your sons to respect women!
34. Model a belief that prayer works. Keep a prayer journal and celebrate God's answers regularly.
35. Model generosity for those in need.
36. Model spiritual involvement in the lives of people rejected by the world.
37. Model visiting the shut-ins, those in prison, and the lonely.
38. Model financial sacrifice for the spiritual training of children. They will see if vacation spending trumps_____.
39. Model joy, enthusiasm, and note-taking during sermons.
40. Keep Scripture and Christian music playing at home and in the car.

Joe Brumfield

Questions Women Ask When Their Husband Is Looking At Porn:

1. Why is my husband looking when he has me?
2. Why does this makes me feel so inadequate!
3. This is the same hurt that I felt when my dad betrayed me by...
4. Is it my fault in some way?
5. Would it be better if I gave him more sex?
6. It is true that I don't want sex much, but..is that the reason?
7. Would the problem be fixed if I looked like the women in the pictures?
8. How much of this is my husband's fault?
9. How much of this is specifically from Satan?
10. Do I have to take him back if I love God?
11. Why is this a chemical addiction for him?
12. If I take him back, will I be betrayed again?
13. Should I stay in the relationship for him? For Me?   For God?
14. How much of this is about me?
15. How much of my hurt is really coming from my past, instead of his porn addiction?
16. How much of his porn addiction is because he was set up by his relationships with his dad, his past, ...etc?
17. The research says that if you work through this, you will have a better marriage than you can imagine? Will it really work?
18. If he continues in this behavior without repenting, will he go to hell?
19. Why must I understand the three parts of porn addiction:
    a. The chemical addiction
    b. The emotional intravenous injection of respect
    c. The physical pleasure addiction

20. What lies is Satan telling him to allow this behavior to continue?

21. Am I following a pattern of checking out of relationships, because of the pain that my dad put me through?

103

What Media Does to Families

1. Desensitizes them to violence, immorality, and
     anti-God sentiment
2. Increases their vocabulary--less comprehension
3. Gives them the same values about marriage, sex,
     money, power, humor, family... as is depicted in
     media content
4. Makes media lifestyles, values seem to be "Normal!"
5. Exposes kids to early to....
6. Defines what is "in" and what is politically and socially
     incorrect
7. Makes us more aware of the bad things that are going on
     around the world
8. Dilutes the moral values learned from parents and
     Churches with opposing and conflicting values
9. Makes kids long to be stars and sports heroes
10. Suggests that ones value lies in whether or not they
     have either beauty, brains, brawn (muscle) or bucks
11. Diminishes children's creativity and imagination by
     providing it all for them in media form
12. Causes less work and activity
13. Diminishes family time
14. Lessens time spent reading
15. Cuts out other "free" time activities such as family time
16. Reinforces Consumer culture- teaches the art of
     comparison shopping: Ford vs Chevy, Tide vs Cheer
     coke vs pepsi, your wife versus Cindy Crawford...
17. Teaches that you have a choice--you do not have to stay
     in the situation you are in (Money, marriage, job...)
18. Increases dissatisfaction with one's current state

104

19. Encourages Vicarious participation in romantic, detective, mystery plots (suggests that if you do it only in your mind, it can't hurt you)

20. Increases artificial relationships and easy entertainment over the sweat and tears of working to build <u>real relationships!</u>

21. Assists in avoidance of problem resolution in relationships by giving a cheap substitute: emotional pornography, romance novels, best seller paperbacks, etc.

22. Provides selfish enjoyment through
    a. an escape from reality
    b. easy fulfillment of desires w/ carnal enjoyment
    c. Excuses to not deal with real life, work, relationships
    d. Fantasy fun, sex, danger, bullets, intrigue
    f. Myth of sin without sinning

23. Uses up 13 years of your life

105

Rationalizations For Selfish Media Consumption
Collected by Dr Joe Brumfield 1998-2005

1. I am an adult—I can handle it!
2. I can take the good and throw out the bad.
3. The people watching with me are mature—I don't have to influence them so I can stay.
4. This is how real life is: cursing, violence, sex, etc.
5. I don't want to be naïve.
6. I will not be a party pooper by complaining about the movie.
7. I paid good money to watch this, so I will stay and get my money's worth!
8. Movies are an art form and I'm an art lover—I ignore negative content.
9. This show was based on good literature.
10. It is based on true history (that makes it all right!)
11. It is a true story.
12. It is really, really funny!
13. This movie won top awards.
14. My favorite actor is in it.
15. It is the American way: Men, beer, sports, cheerleaders, movies…
16. Doctors say that Television can be a good stress reliever.
17. I don't approve, but this is just entertainment.
18. It is not like I am going to go out and do some of this stuff—come on, get real! Can you imagine me with a chainsaw or kissing a woman other than my wife?
19. This movie has an excellent message which cancels out the bad stuff.
20. It won't hurt anyone! No one will ever know what I watched!
21. Everyone else saw it.
22. I'm just watching it—this is keeping me from actual adultery, or something worse—consider it a better substitute.
23. I can't afford to be ignorant.
24. It is just to spice up my love life with my spouse—God would like that.
25. I'm an adult—I would never let kids watch this stuff!
26. Nude women do not offend me—it is natural—you have the problem!
27. The sex and violence were not real—it is just pretend blood

106

Rules for Dealing With Media In Our Family
1. All Media viewing must be planned in advance
2. Only ____ hours of television may be watched per day.
3. All homework and chores must be done first.
4. We only watch shows that we believe Jesus would watch.
   (All media consumed must bring glory to God)
5. We say "boo" when someone on television says or does
   something that a Christian shouldn't say or do.
6. We play "spot the lie" in order to become very careful
   consumers of media. Kids get a nickel for every wrong
   message or bad word they spot for their vacation fund, or
   college fund jar.
7. Kids do not see any shows or listen to any music that parents
   haven't previewed. We are as concerned with spiritual
   germs that infect the soul as we are of physical germs that
   infect the body. We don't let our kids drink out of the toilet
   either.
8. No meals will be eaten with the television on.
9. No radios or televisions in the children's bedrooms.
10. Positive Christian music will be kept playing in the home
    as "background music."
11. Kids do not go to friends houses to watch television or listen
    to music without parents specific consent.
12. Parents will watch media with children.
13. Parents will keep a good supply of great music and movies on
    hand.
14. Kids will not be given portable radios with earphones. Any
    music good enough for children is good enough for parents
15. Parents will verbally counter every message in music or on
    television that they disagree with.
16. Parents and children will discuss and pray together about
    media influences on a regular basis.
17. Parents will discourage their children's association with peers
    who consume media without careful Christian supervision.

Brumfield

107

Good Effects of Media
1. A great educational tool
2. Reaches the masses
3. Consumers feel safe while listening (non-threatening)
4. Can be used as a babysitter if great programs are
     selected in advance
5. A great evangelistic tool
6. Can be very cost effective
7. Reaches audiences that can't be otherwise reached
8. Can help a person learn what is going on in the world
9. Counseling tool
10. Very visual impact teaches better than mere lecturing
11. Bible study can be increased
12. Can provide valuable family entertainment
13. Can bring cultures together
14. Warn of weather and military dangers
15. Government information is available
16. Very powerful method of swaying public opinion

108

Subconscious Media Messages

1. Physical appearance is everything
2. Life must always be fun
3. Intimacy = Sex = Happiness
4. Love conquers all
5. You can't have fun if you aren't being entertained
6. Falling in love leads to a happy ending
7. "Everybody" who is normal has sex (except nerds)
8. Violence is thrilling to watch: wrestling, hitting, tackling, bombing, shooting, etc.
9. If you don't have what you want: take it by force
10. Children "need" to be made happy
11. There is some good in all "filth"
12. Youth is everything--fight to stay young
13. If it feels good, looks good, tastes good---do it, touch it, use it, eat it...
14. It is normal to sow your wild oats
15. If it isn't producing enjoyment--bail out!!
16. Parents are stupid
17. We have rights and deserve to be happy
18. Religion is for narrow minded bigots, fanatics, and ignorant people
19. Everybody's views should be tolerated
20. God doesn't belong in the public sector
21. Athiesm is the religion of the politically and socially enlightened
22. Truth is totally subjective

Brumfield

109

23. There is "Adult" entertainment, and there is "Child" entertainment

24. Individuals aren't responsible for their bad actions--it is the result of their family and environment

25. If you have been mistreated by a spouse, you have a right to be happy

26. It is right to make any choice that feels like it will lead to happiness

27. You are one product from happiness

28. Skinny women are sexy, fat ones are ugly

29. People without Beauty, or Brains, or Brawn, or Bucks are worthless

30. It is wrong to criticize anything about the homosexual lifestyle

31. Go for the gusto, just do it, run toward happiness

32. Material possessions bring happiness

33. It is right to get vengeance if "they deserve it"

34. It is right to overcome evil with violence--it is a successful method

35. "Real women" are very sexually aggressive

36. Dangerous and risky activities are more enjoyable

37. Sex is more fun if you aren't supposed to, and if you aren't married to your partner (Stolen water is sweet)

38. Woman's only value is as a sex object--the less "Sexy" a woman is, the less valuable she is

Brumfield

39. Changing partners regularly can make life exciting, and fulfilling
40. Sex humor is funnier
41. Married life is boring, and unfulfilling--everybody eventually gets a divorce--everybody cheats ...

Brumfield

HOW TO SOLVE A PROBLEM

1. Decide exactly what the problem is, and discuss it until you can agree what the problem is that needs solved. Write the problem to be solved here:

2. Pick a good time, and place to work on the problem, and schedule it now. Time:
   Place:

3. List at least three things you have tried to solve the problem:
   a.
   b.
   c.

4. Tell how you have helped to cause part of the problem:
   person #1 One thing I have done that has helped to cause this problem or made it worse is:

   person #2 same:
   **DO NOT EXPLAIN WHY IT IS NOT YOUR FAULT AT THIS POINT.
   Do not argue or discuss your personal feelings yet either.

5. List all possible solutions to this problem. Let your mind run wild.
   Do not discuss the pros and cons of any possible solution yet.
   Just list them:

6. Choose the best possible one and tell how you feel about each one.

7. Write out a plan for achieving it (in detail)
   include answers to who? When? Why? How much? How?, What?
   Where, and any other details. List a time to begin, and a completion time.

8. Our first step is:

9. List a method of accountability:

10. Pray about it together daily.

Honest Apologies Give New Life To Relationships

Date and marry someone who often says, " that was my fault" "I messed up!" "My Bad"---avoid dating people who blame someone or something-----avoid them like the plague! JSB

"Real Men (and women) are quick to accept full responsibility for their mistakes----weak men make excuses, and attempt to wiggle out of blame" JSB

1. Admit your mistake. When you apologize to your spouse, you give a new possible future to your relationship!

2. Say you are sorry and really mean it. Fake apologies just add emotional baggage and resentment.

3. Take responsibility
4. Repenting—share your desire to never repeat the offense---I don't want to ever do this again---could you help me think of ways to avoid this problem I
5. Asking for forgiveness: Be very clear about it!!

6. <u>Parenting the language of Apology:</u>
    Teach kids to apologize:
    a. Teach them to say, "I broke the lamp" Not , "the lamp broke"
    b. Teach them that their behavior always effects other people.
    c. There are always rules in life kids---live by the rules and you will have a better life.
    d. If you break the rules---there are consequences

    e. Saying, "I'm sorry but…" is childish! "But," means that I am not willing to take full responsibility for my part of the problem.

112

SECRET HURTS FROM PAST SEXUAL ABUSE

Dr. Joe Brumfield 2001

Possible feelings of the victim:

1. I feel like it was my fault someway
2. If people knew the truth about me, they would never treat me as normal.
3. I feel worthless and dirty--I don't deserve anyone good to love me.
4. How could God ever forgive me?
5. I even "enjoyed" some of the bad things.
6. I wanted them to do it (it made me feel valuable and loved)
7. My body betrayed me (I didn't want it to feel good)
8. I hate myself for sometimes enjoying something so dirty and wicked
9. I must be wicked if I felt good or wanted attention
10. I have to be constantly on guard so no one finds out
11. I feel a constant sense of shame and guilt
12. Somebody will find out—if I ever find a spouse they won't love me if they find out—I must keep it buried a t all costs
13. Nobody will ever love me if they know the real me

14. If I ever find somebody to love me—it won't last
15. I both want sex and hate sex now—I can't stand how I feel either way
16. I feel depressed, and numb
17. I can't seem to show emotions
18. I sometimes have flashbacks
19. have a fear of sex, or emotional closeness

With commentary by Dr. Brumfield

1. Cosmo and junk in the grocery store
2. 101 sex tips—sexually saturated culture
3. America: sexual stimuli overload: billboards, --you can't even watch football without being bombarded
4. Culture says: sexually anything goes…if over 18..as long as you and your partner are OK with it
5. viewing sexual activity is the #1 sexual activity
6. 21 million Americans 1 in 4 Americans visits a sex site monthly
7. hurting productivity 2 of 3 companies have disciplined employees
8. 9-5 weekdays is the highest traffic time for porn
9. 12 billion dollars more than Americans spend prof football, baseball, basketball and hockey
10. combined playboy and penthouse circulation exceeds that of the combined circulation of Time and Newsweek combined (even with net porn available
11. the largest consumers are teenagers
12. **THIS THE NORM FOR OUR TEENAGERS LEARNING ABOUT SEXUALITY: NOT PARENTS, THE CHURCH, OR THE SCHOOL**
13. What about women: sexuality is their greatest asset:
    a. Sexy chick sells cars, light bulbs, etc
    b. Female's who are smart will capitalize on this
    c. Use your sexuality to get what you want
    d. "today's woman is liberated"---
        i. Birth control pill
        ii. Abortion prevalence
        iii. Woman can choose anything she wants sexually
        iv. Sex should always be exciting for him!!!!
        v. Glamor magazine title: 20 things you'll be happy you tried in bed, and he will too…
        vi. Cosomo: mattress moves so good that he'll forget his name but remembers yours forever
        vii. Culture: women are to be sexually aggressive
        viii. Sex in the city, "why can't women have sex like a man,…idea: no strings attached……go for it, get what you want….be aggressive…
        ix. Assumed that if you are dating, and like somebody, we are being sexual..this is how we show affection

    x.   **Our culture says that sex is the highest form of affection "I only sleep with people that I really like…a committed relationship…if we are in love…if we are really compatible…"**

    xi. **Created enormous sexual power for women—they learn to use sex to get what they want**

    xii. **Draw a picture of your addiction: describe: I am the princess in the middle and I have lots of sexual admirers…go into a bar…spend the evening going back and forth to the restroom and counting the number of visual hits she could get, "It just made me feel like I was worth something"**

e. **Fashion has followed our sexual focus: look what women are wearing: Seminar leader puts dress code in her advertising brochures**

f. **Cosmetics over 20 billion a year in America spent by women**

g. **70% of plastic surgery people are from families with household incomes of less than 60,000 Tennessean NewsPaper from yesterday "Cosmetic Surgery for the Masses"**

h. **People are desperately trying to keep up with looks**

i. **80% of women are dissatisfied withtheir looks**

j. **5 foot 10inches 115 lbs average model**

k. **5 feet 4inches 145 lbs average women in US**

l. **25 % of men and 45% of women are on a diet**

m. **Majority of them will gain the weight back**

n. **Our culture is effecting promiscuity**

o. **61 % of HS seniors report that they are having sex**

p. **"I wanted to repeat that feeling of being loved, he told me I was special, and that I was pretty**

q. **Confusion between sex and love**

r. **Sex was what was going to make me think I was OK**

s. **50% of HS Seniors say they are continuing sex**

t. **21% of HS have had 4 or more sexual partners**

u. **We are changing our definition of sex…."I did not have sex with that woman?**

v. **More that half of teens have had oral sex, but do not consider it "sex" still consider themselves virgins**

w. **Ways we try to justify our own guilt…we will drink and have oral sex…and we are not being sexual…we are virgins**

x. Demographics…its not the "bad kids" broken home kids, those from the "projects" statistically: they are above avg in income and education, and they are white [12c]

y. Doesn't stop in marriage: marrying the right person does not take care of your promiscuity

z. Thought getting married to the right guy would fix all my problems….available, and moral sexual partner

aa. I took all of my baggage—and took it to my husband,and I said, "here, fix this!!"

bb. I didn't know what the problem was, but I knew I felt terrible inside

cc. I thought marriage would fill the huge black hole inside of me….like the movies

dd. I discovered He couldn't fill it…I felt worse and worse, now I felt tricked…I reverted to old mechanisms…trying to get my needs met through relationships which always turned sexual..

ee. Of course it was my husband's fault….blamed my many affairs on him

ff. 14 -19 % are in an affair now   40 t 60 % say they have had an affair…not just sex addicts….average disenchanted woman…grass looks greener

gg. We are not talking about single one time mistakes   15 %of woman have had more that 4 affairs

hh. 11.5% of women have had an affair with another woman

ii. Our culture is shaping our women

jj. The internet is one of the biggest shaper…supercharges sex in our culture: anonymous, affordable, tons of free stuff, very accessible, supposedly victimless (JSB)

kk. Internet is opening a "save" world of exploration for women

ll. 1 in 3 internet porn visitors is female

mm. Esp younger women are looking at Visual Porn…

nn. Sexual chat rooms—good church women

oo. Christianity Today: 34% of women who answered their survey admitted to accessing porn

pp. "To me it feels like I am enslaved and chained to the computer" We just wanted join the modern culture…our kids were supposed to do internet research for school

qq. "In two months, I was consumed with internet porn"

rr. She termed herself "a sexual addict"

ss. 8-10 % of our population (up to 20%) are addicted

tt. 1/3 of them are females;....not scary "man" in trench coat

uu.   What does it mean to be sexually addicted:

1. def: from Dr. Pat Carnes:
2. an addiction to have a pathological (sick) relationship pattern of behavior
3. begins with the sinful choice to commit sexual sin!!!
4. You can be a sexual sinner and not be committed
5. My ongoing pattern makes me an addict with a mood altering substance, experience
6. Sexual addiction has been removed from the DSM4 ---used to be in the DSM
7. Substitute the word sex ---in the DSM under "Gambling Addiction"
8. Characteristics of Addiction
    a. It is obsessive—always on my my mind— it is what organizes my life
       Always thinking about my affair partner
       i. I wouldn't leave my home for fear that He might call
       ii. What lie do I tell
       iii. How do I get over the guilt I feel
    b. It is compulsive—I do what I hate--I can't do what I want...what a wretched man I am
    c. I stopped 57 times—I couldn't stay stopped--- red flags
    d. Addictive behavior keeps going despite
    e. negative consequences
    f. You had your 3rd DUI—why do you continue
    g. When people keep doing things that hurt them terribly, and they still can't stop
9. Tolerance: can have coffee in the evening with no effect---learn to tolerate behavior----sexual thoughts changes brain chemistry—not just sexual activity
10. serotonin, dopamine, adrenylin, oxytocin (touch) feel good chemicals---the brain adjusts

and becomes tolerant like to alcohol---it takes ^{12e} more and more and more to get the same effect

11. Relationship addict: (love addict) one after another after another addict...keeps someone stringing along—in case this one doesn't work
12. You can have a sexual addiction without being sexual
13. Romance addiction: flowers..lasts 2-4 wks
14. Women are in it for the chase
15. Porn addict... strip clubs, selling sex for dinner, tickets, looking at visual porn in , compulsive masturbating...many porn addict women masturbate....
16. Many women partner with another sex addict----not a codependent.....both are addicts
17. Lots of emotional pain involved...
18. They do not tell you they are a sex addict...so look for signs and concurrent condictions:
    a. Depression,
    b. Dystemic: Eyore in Winnie the Pooh---just don't feel god
    c. Adjustment disorder-
    d. Substance use or dependence- toblock inhibitions or medicate guilt
    e. Post tramautic stress disorder
    f. Eating disorders---sex and food addicts can go back and forth
    g. Ask specifically about relationships and sexual behavior---she will not bring it up
    h. Predictible cycle:
        i. Always fantasizing
        ii. Rituals: dress and appearance
        iii. Flirting
        iv. Despair—"I've done this again—after I promised God"—need more medication -Be great mom—focused on my kids—be very spiritual...
        v. Lose job—slept with the boss—
        vi. Lost job—internet use
        vii. Unplanned pregnancy

Family Problem Resolution Plan

1. Choose one night of the week, and stay at the table after the meal is finished. Each family member then gives one compliment to every one else at the table. After everyone has complimented each other, a prayer should follow where God's blessings are asked for each one present.

2. Give appreciation to family members when you see them doing something good during the day.

3. Choose a night during the week and have each family member fill in the following sentences during or after the meal:

   a. One thing I really need from the rest of you is....
   b. I have been frustrated lately by...
   c. One thing that has really encouraged me is...
   d. I wish all of you would pray for me this week about...
   f. I think the Devil is trying to get me by...
   g. One thing someone did this week that really helped me was
   h. On a scale of one to ten:
      -my relationship with God today is a _____
      -I feel loved by all of you at a _____
      -I feel accepted at school by my peers at a _____
      - I would rate the way I like myself at a _____
      - My emotional bank for today is about_____
   i. One thing that happened in the past that really hurt me was
      _____ and I would rate the hurt at a_____ (0
      means not much hurt and 10 is terrible
   j. I feel like God has been ignoring me when.....
   k. When I think about spiritual matters, I sometimes wonder if...
   l. I would enjoy life and my family lots more if...

   Brumfield and D.Smith Dec 99

Conflict Predictor: Communicating About Our Passions, Our Past, and Our Priorities

1. How much do you care about God compared to how much you care about me?

2. What are 5 things you want to do differently with your future family than your parents did?

3. What are 5 things that you want to do the same or similar to your family? (both should share)

4. How has Satan attacked you and your heart in the past? (see Dr. Brumfield's list)

5.   How do you think Satan will try to destroy you in the future?

6. What are Satan's lies that you have believed about yourself?

7. Put the following desires in your personal priority order and then discuss how your differences might impact your marriage:

 desire for financial success, family security, knowing I'm loved, having some of the nicer things in life, being respected by the people around me, family, etc, physical safety, spending more family time together, having fun, accomplishing something worthwhile with my life.

Why Do Some People Explode With Anger?
(Share—don't Stuff your feelings!!)

Some people are so afraid of conflict, that they hold their true feelings inside: stuffers—Volcano loaders!!

1. **Pretending that your feelings aren't hurt, (refusing to share your true heart with your family hurts them) or pretending that you aren't angry is not Christlike!! Jesus said, "Go to your brother!!"**
2. **People that don't "STUFF" to be Christlike, often go to the other extreme, and strike out in anger, …they vent all over you….rage…hurt, harsh words…**
3. The way to peace in relationships is not yelling, and it is not hiding and pretending! God wants us to share in a healthy way! **"SPEAK THE TRUTH IN LOVE"**
4. **The hurts that you buried…the resentments, the anger….will eventually come to come to the surface, and it will damage all of your other relationships!**
5. **(Unresolved Conflicts) Communication Intensive always damages your kids.**
6. **Unresolved Baggage kills close relationships.**
7. **Oh…Yes, I'm the great pretender!!**

Everybody longs for deep connections with other people!
Someone has said, "Intimacy is shared privacy."

Only those people who allow themselves to be transparent and honest about their own "private" selves, can be safe for other people to approach!

People who hide themselves to play it safe, build walls around them that their spouse, friends, and own family cannot scale. They tell themselves that they are hiding anger, hurts, fears, resentments, so they don't upset people, and kill relationships, but the opposite is true!!

Try a message that starts out with **"I feel"**
YOU messages blame, and get people ready to fight.
> **You Always or Your Never---Doubles the ATTACK!!!**

> Focus on yourself instead of on them!!!

Try: In situation A, when you do B, It feel C!! "When we're at church, And you talk to the young pretty girls, I feel betrayed!"

114

Which of these is <u>your</u> counseling goal for this session?

1. Getting acquainted and breaking the ice?
2. Collecting information about the problem(s)?
3. Helping the client understand how things in the past may have caused the problem?
4. Helping the client get an objective view of self and the problem?
5. Building the client's communication skills.
6. Being a catalyst for a behavior change?
7. Helping the client reach their greatest personal potential?
8. Helping the client find values and goals far greater than themselves?
9. Encouraging the client so they can survive the present crisis?
10. Facilitating the client's discovering their own solutions?
11. Motivating the client toward some objective?
12. Helping a client stop or slow a negative behavior?
13. Assisting a client to admit the real issues so they can deal with them?
14. Provoking a client to stop running from the problem, but to stand and deal with it?
15. Helping the client find help and hope from God?

IF YOU DO NOT KNOW WHAT YOUR GOAL IS FOR THIS SESSION, HOW WILL YOU KNOW WHICH DIRECTION TO GO?

Dr. Joe Brumfield
McRae, Arkansas
February 19, 1998

115

10 Things To Do For A Christian Marriage On The Brink

1. Get Radical!   Deal with this now!   Your soul and the souls of your children are in jeopardy. Disconnect the phone, break off all social engagements- Take time off from work to deal with your marriage problems. You may be too exhausted, or have too little time after working all day. Go ahead and use your vacation time--this is an emergency!! Take the kids to Grandma's -Your marriage mending needs your full attention and must take to priority.   "Half baked" efforts will likely produce "half baked" solutions.

2. Commit to God and your spouse, that you will complete whatever process of counseling, or growth needed without quitting, or without making any major decisions about divorce or separation. Commit to be faithful to your spouse during the counseling process--give God a chance to work.

3. Commit to confidentiality! Promise that you won't "blab" negative or private things about your spouse to friends or coworkers.

4. Commit to pray for and with your spouse on a daily basis. Pray for God's help when you rise in the morning, when you first meet in the evening, and right before going to bed. Ask God to help you base your love on Him, and not on your fickle feelings. Ask for peace, and for protection from the Devil.

5. Spend at least 30 minutes every evening studying the Bible together. Read a version that is easy to understand.

6. Attend church services together every time the doors are opened--even when you don't feel like it, and even when you feel hypocritical. Ask God to help your heart.

7. List your unconfessed (hidden sins)-- now confess them to God and Spouse. Sincerely apologize for every wrong you are aware of.

116

10 Things To Do For A Christian Marriage On The Brink cont.

8. Write out a list of reasons you appreciate your spouse. (Strong points) If your love bank is totally depleted now, list the things that you loved about them when you first started dating, and when you first married.

9. Write out a list of things that you think may be bothering your spouse about you. (Both spouses should do this)
   -
   -
   -
   -
   -

   A. have your spouse add anything bothering them that you may have Left off

   -
   -
   -
   -

   B. Each spouse should now rate the problems listed in order of their importance: #1 is the thing that has been upsetting me the most...

   #1

   #2

   #3

   #4

   #5

10. Read together all of the Bible verses you can find about God's plans for marriages and families.

117

Common Questions Asked by Christian University Students

1. How do I know which religion is right?
2. Is it possible for more than one church to be OK with God?
3. Does the Bible specifically say that I can't have sex before marriage?
4. How far is too far on a date, or before marriage?
5. If I have sinned sexually, and have asked God to forgive me, am I a virgin in God's sight?
6. Do I have to tell my fiancée about my sexual sins of the past, especially when God has already forgiven me?
7. Should a virgin marry a non-virgin?
8. Is Baptism really essential? How do we know whether or not God will count sprinkling or pouring? When do I need to be rebaptized?
9. When is it OK to get a divorce? When is it OK to get remarried?
10. Will a person go to hell for using instruments in church? At home?
11. Can I marry a divorced person for any reason?
12. At what point does God require me to leave my second or third spouse, and go back to my first spouse?
13. Does the Church of Christ have a monopoly on salvation?
14. Is there any absolute truth? (Is even Jimmy Allen right?)
15. Are some things "grey" and some things "black and white?"
16. What can women do in the church, and what can they not do?
17. What does submission mean for women? Was it a cultural thing? Do women have to submit to all men, or only to their husbands? When can a woman teach men? When can a woman baptize someone?
18. Do men ever have to submit? When?
19. Is it wrong to marry someone of a different skin color?
20. How do I know who God has picked for me to marry?
21. Where did different races come from? Why did God make people look different? What is a Christian view of racism?
22. How do I know when I am ready to get married?
23. Is there more than one good spouse out there for me?
24. Will God direct me to the right person If I ask Him?
25. Does God give any kind of signs today so I'll know?
26. Can I still be forgiven for a premeditated sin?
27. Have I committed the unforgivable sin?
28. Is it too late for me to be forgiven?
29. How do I forgive other people? Myself???
30. If I don't feel forgiven, does that mean that I am not forgiven?
31. Should I go to church, take the Lord's Supper, pray, etc, If I don't feel spiritual, or If I don't feel forgiven, or If I haven't been living right in my relationship with God? Is it hypocritical to act right, if I don't feel it?

Questions formulated by Dr. Joe Brumfield April, 1998

118

Homosexuality: Can It Be Prevented?

Focus on the Family Notes for March 31-April 2, 2003
Guest: Dr. Joseph Nicolosi knows this issue better than anyone Dobson is aware of.
Director of NARTH (National Association for Research and Treatment of
Homosexuality) Dr. Nicolosi believes that homosexuality is preventable and that it is not
predetermined, or caused by genetics.
Book: <u>A Parents Guide To Preventing Homosexuality</u>: gives their collection of research
and scientific facts.
Other popular books on Raising boys say do nothing except support your boy if he has
these tendencies
Fact: most parents given the choice would rather their kids be heterosexual—it is easier
Gender Identity Disorder: boy w/wrong identity action, girls who are tom boys...

It is possible in many or most cases to prevent homosexuality
- developmental gaps in parent child relationship are seen
- it is not genetic tho it may be influenced by genetic traits
- there may be temperamental dispositions
- it is primarily a developmental problem
- a child who is secure in their gender identity gives best assurance
  of heterosexual development later
- Developmental Roots of Homosexuality Typically:
    1. boy has to identify with father and dis-identify with mother at early stage
    2. at 15-18 months (gender identity phase) notices difference—which am I?
        a. He wants to fulfill his masculinity—needs support of mom and dad
        b. Mother has to support his becoming a man—not hold boys too tightly
        c. More danger if mom and dad aren't getting along well
        d. Father has to welcome son into masculine identity
        e. If Father and Son Bond—he will not make a fantasy attempt to
           connect with the masculine---He will actually have a real bond!

    *Other researchers disagree with Nicolosi. Some claim that
    Homosexuality is caused by genetics. Some research suggests
    Genetic predisposition but not genetic causation.

119

Pathological Circumstances of Homosexuality
(From the Nicolosi View)

- Dad is distant, gone, alcoholic, won't bond with a sensitive, non-athletic son— or artistic son, --No good bond between Father and son
- Father son relationship is key
- When dad comes home from work—if son is happy to see him—dad makes him feel happy—if dad is affirming—no problems likely with son becoming homosexual,
- But if son trys to stay away from father and there is a negative feeling—he transfers it to other men---leery detachment and fear of being a part—boy wants to connect with the masculine but fears—so he decides to do it through fantasy

Certain Signs of Pre Homosexuality describe Childhood GID
Show Strong (pp. 40 in Nicolosi's book:)Predictability:
(75% coorelation between these actions and homosexuality, and other similar sexual problems)

1. Repeatedly stated desire to be other sex or act like other sex
2. Strong Preference for cross dressing or pretending to dress like other gender
3. Strong and persistence desire for opposite roles
4. Wants games and pastimes of other sex
5. Strong preference for playmates of the other sex

"Mothers make boys, and Fathers make men"—Nicolosi
Have to have some male role to facilitate transition to masculine identity
Robert Stoller from UCLA says "Masculinity is an achievement"
Our Culture is losing separate things for boys that help boys decide to be masculine and give clear difference

Single Mothers:Cub scouts and male Sunday school class is not enough to help a boy reach a clear gender identity:
The boy must have one salient (good and strong) man who takes a special intere: in Him—One male chooses him---
Men: find those fatherless boys and invite them to go fishing—Play catch with him---especially the quiet boy in the background….the one in the background--- the one that nobody notices--- He is the one we have to go after

120

The Development of Homosexual Behavior according to Dr. Nicolosi
(From Homosexual Clients' Testimony)
Classic triangle relationship:
1. Over involved intrusive domineering mother, 2. uninvolved father,
3. shy boy (usually developed by 3 years) but can be changed

Dads get involved and Moms back off   "One sentence Rx   Kid was turned off and surrendered his masculine strivings: Dad has to make son see him as important (father was weak, or abusive—a big negative force---impotent)

Dad, take the boy out of the house—just you and he—take him with you---wrestle with Him---needs physicality---Dad tuck him in at night—tell him stories about your youth---pray with him---turn the light out

Entice the boy away from that super bond with mom---come on kid, being a man is fun--Mom should not interfere—don't get in the way of the father son relationship

Don't communicate between mom and dad

Mom's talk dad up to the kids

Danger: Mother does not respect the Father—boy is bad" mom says, "you're just like your father

Danger: kid surrenders his masculine strivings, and at age 5 and 6 other boys notice because they are resisting their own feminine pull
If Father
Three A's of Homosexuals Unmet needs by Dad: Attention, Affection, and Approval If it is not possible from Dad, kids give up trying to be Masculine and just fantasize and eroticize some masculinity instead

Need a Man to go with them and show boys where the masculinity is inside them

121

Is Same Sex Attraction Related to Relationship between Father and Son?

"I have never seen a homosexual who had a loving, respectful
relationship with his father" says Dr. Nicolosi
(also quoted by 60's research expert, Ervin Beaver)

Same issue with lesbians, just more subtle—early hurt in relationship with mother
Male homosexual is totally consumed with their sexuality (it is a reparative drive)
--trying to solve fundamental issues that have nothing to do with sex , it's about longing,
about emotional abandonment, conquering, reducing anxiety, emotional attachment,
reducing depression

Homosexuality is not about sex—it is about trying to get all these other emotional needs
met--like identification: Identity is a core drive for a person: "who am I"

They are trying to find their masculine identity through sex
Around Age 12 or-13 called the Erotic transitional phase: all the emotional needs of who
am I , my emotional needs, identification, belonging ---all these psychological issues now
merge with sex when sexual feelings began to come –now the kid finds himself attracted t
boys—they have a certain quality, a mystery, a fascination--- (there is something exciting
about boys, but I feel inferior and I can't be one of them or connect with them even
though I want to be one)—I feel ill equipped to be one of them.   This sense of tension
becomes eroticized.

Lots of 15 and 16 yr olds in therapy now—10 yrs ago most of our clients were in their
twenties and thirties—now we are getting them much younger, 14 yrs old etc
"This is a very difficult age to treat"

Implications of having a school counselor say to confused kid "you must accept this –you
will always be this way---I guess you have a gay gene"---JUNK Damages kid
Gay will become their identity if fed, confirmed---on the net, etc… California schools are
doing this in kindergarten…   only 2% of population is gay---but it will become 10%
because society is rapidly laying the foundation

Parents can prevent homosexuality---there is a choice---there is something you can do!!!
You don't have do just let schools do this to your kid
Talk to your kid about your values Kids are being pressured to become what will cause
them horrible pain all their lives

Letter to A Father From His Abandoned Daughter

Dear Daddy,

Every little girl needs her daddy and I need you to be my daddy. I have always loved you, and I miss you. In spite of all the bad things that have happened I have not quit loving you. I feel so hurt because you abandoned me and because I feel that you constantly do things to hurt me and our family.

What I have really longed for you to do is say you are sorry and try to build a relationship with me. I know we can't undo all of the hurts of the past, but I wish I could forgive you and we could start over. No matter what happens I love you, and I want to see you in heaven some day. I know that the Devil wants you to believe that you have no hope but that is not true.

Carrying this hurt around for so long has made me emotionally weak and caused me to search for love in other places. I miss you so much--I don't understand why you keep hurting me--I just want to know that you love me.
It hurts me greatly to hurt you, --I just don't want to carry it around anymore. I just want to be able to forgive you and stop carrying the hurt. This hurt is controlling my life and ruining all of my relationships. I can't seem to trust anyone--especially a guy. I have this horrible fear that this same terrible thing will happen to
my family. It makes me feel set apart from people because I am from a broken home. I find myself questioning God. I know that God is not the reason this happened, but I just don't know why He would let something like this happen.

I am not asking for things to be the same. I know that you and mom are remarried and that things can never be like they once were—although I dream about it happening still. You are still my father whether or not you divorced mom. You didn't divorce me! The divorce was really painful but the fact that you both still fight after so many years makes it worse. It seems so ridiculous that you can't get along.

I want to know what you are thinking. I want to know what happened. I know you won't tell me everything, but I need to understand. We seemed to be such a Christ centered family at one time. It just all fell apart and my life has been in a daze for the last several years.

I want to be able to talk to you like I once did--like your my dad. This is how it should be. I feel like you don't care about me because you talk to your step kids, but you don't talk to me.

I don't yet feel like you deserve forgiveness, but I want to quit hating you and being so angry with you. I know that God forgives us all when we don't deserve it, so I am going to give all my pain to God and ask Him to help me forgive you.

I know that God longs for you to come back to Him. Some may think you are too proud, but I hope you won't let your pride get in the way of seeing what is really important. If only you could tell me that you still love me and that you are sorry for what you did to me.

I am giving this burden back to you because I don't deserve to carry it around. I am tired of it and I want to move on. Now that I'm grown, I am looking for my future husband. I know that I need to settle things with you before I move into a marriage--because I don't want to carry all of this hurt and pain into my marriage and have something bad like this happen in my own marriage.

You know that just because I forgive you--that doesn't mean I am going to call your new wife my step mom or develop a relationship with her, but I would like a relationship with you.

I still think about you every day and I pray that God will soften your heart and open your eyes--and that we will be able to build a healthy relationship.
I still love you even though you hurt me   Your daughter forever

Love Letter To Dad Brings Powerful Motivation For Change

Dear Daddy,

I love you so very much! I have been thinking about how much I love you, and how rarely I have told you. We never know when our last time on earth will be, and I want to tell you some important things: I know that you love me, even though you have probably been taught not to say it much. Every word of love from you fills my heart with joy, and heals so many of the hurts that the devil wants me to keep.

Thank you for working so hard and sending me to to a Christian School. I am a lot like you, and I work very hard. Thank you for this great lesson. Thank you for growing. Many kids here have Fathers who are too proud to continue to grow spiritually--and they become just like him.

I know that you show your love to me in many ways, and that you tell me in little ways when it is not too uncomfortable. Thank you for loving me enough to go against tradition to make me feel loved and safe and secure.

One of my teachers talks about how the relationship between a daughter and her father has a lot to do with how she views God. Fathers who show love, kindness, and forgiveness help one trust God. Most of the famous athiests in the world had fathers who did not show love and affection to them. I'm so glad that you do not abandon me and betray me like so many of their fathers did.

I want to marry a man someday that has many of the good qualities that you have: one that wants to please God, one that is not afraid to change and grow, even though it is very uncomfortable and difficult, one that is honest, and hard working, one that prays often for his family, and so many other things.

I will try to follow your example of loving, and working, and growing. I know I may have a streak of pride, but I will never stop working on it. I know the Bible says that God resists the proud, but that He gives grace to the humble.

Thank you for loving my mother. You probably tell her a lot more than we know, and that makes me feel safe and secure knowing that my parents love each other, and often tell each other so. I see people all over the world abandoning their mates emotionally, or divorcing them. I am so glad to know that you would never do anything like that.

Well, I just wanted to write and tell you how much I love and appreciate you. I'm sorry that I have been uncomfortable telling you more. May God bless my daddy!

Love,
    Jenny

Sample Apology Letter to Grown Adult Children

1. It is hard for me to come talk to you about these things because...

2. Although it is easy for me to blame my upbringing or _____ circumstances, I take responsibility for...

3. I wish that I had shown you more love by...

4. I'm sorry that I treated your mom/dad...

5. One thing I really wish that I had done more with you is...

6. I wish that I could take back...

7. I know that I hurt God and I hurt you when I ...

8. I have been praying that God would...

9. I am so ashamed that...

10. What could I do so that you would forgive all of the hurts and wrongs that I have caused against you?

11. Will you please pray that I have the courage to...

12. I want us to start a new chapter in our relationship by...

13. I love you so much that...

14. I will love you forever because...

15. My greatest joy will be to see you in heaven because...

16. Please pray for me that God will...

Dr. Joe Brumfield, Sept 2000

Letter of Pain to My Husband:

What I Need to tell you:

Do you want to be married to me or not? I am so tired of hurt.
I know some of the incredible person in you, but it shows so rarely.
I need some closure on a lot of things. I want to go on in life. Do
you want to go on with me or not? Do you still have any dreams for
us in the future? Are you trapped in some problem that I could
help with? Do you ever plan to be a husband to me again, or am
I just a convenient babysitter for the kids, and a person who has
some income that pays the rent? I need to know where I stand!
My stress level has been near the breaking point for a long time.
Where are you? Do you ever want to let the real you out of its
hiding place again? I know you have talents, and intelligence, and
abilities, and many things for a wife and children to be proud of--
but I know that something is holding you back. Are you jealous
that I am going to school? Do you feel safer, or more in control
if I am trapped without education, and doomed to minimum wage
for the rest of my life? What do you want out of our marriage?
Why do you not believe in marriage counselors? What If I found
one that wouldn't charge. You don't have to believe everything
they say, but they might help us move on toward the kind of life
that we always dreamed of. I know that God hates divorce. Part
of me wishes that you would either come home all the way, and
let's have a real family, or that you would just leave permanently.
Please give me some glimmer of hope for the future. What is the
reason that you stay? I never want to take that reason away from
you. I need to know now if you are committed to this marriage or
not. Make your choice! I want you to stay, but you can't just keep
coming and going.

Spouse Confession: My part in our problems:

1. I have become dishonest with you. I am no longer open with you
   and that is not right. I am not supposed to return evil for evil.
2. I hide things from you because I am afraid of how you will react.
3. I don't communicate with you about things.
4. I take full responsibility for the kids, and do not share it with
   you. This may be because of how you treat them.
5. I may be overprotective of the children because of my past.
6. I do all of the disciplining--and do not allow you to help train
   the children like I should.
7. I am not submissive in some things. I do some things even though
   you wish that I would not.
8. I don't show you my real anger sometimes because I am afraid
   that you will feed off my anger. I hide myself and my real
   feelings from you. It is not right for me to refuse to let you
   know my feelings.
9. I put the children before you--and I know that really makes you
   mad. I don't even serve your food first. Instead of putting
   you first, I put the kid's needs first.
10. I may be partially to blame for the fact that you do not want
    the responsibilities of a family--or it may be that you do want
    these responsibilities, but I am taking them from you.
11. I probably still try to compensate for the fact that I took my
    children's father from them. This may be why I do not put
    you first, as perhaps I should. I feel so guilty.
12. My "Package Deal" of marrying you with two kids may make it
    really difficult for you. It may not be fair for you to have to
    treat them like your own. (I am very grateful
    for the love and concern that you have shown toward them)
    I know that a "ready made family" is a great burden.

124

When You Are Considering Divorce:

Common Feelings:

1. I feel terribly betrayed.
2. I doubt that I could ever trust my spouse again.
3. I feel that there has been too much water under the bridge for me to make a come back.
4. Part of me wants to get even.
5. I want them to know and feel the pain that they have caused me.
6. I want to permanently get away from this awful hurt.
7. I have considerable guilt when I think of divorce and what it may do to my children.
8. I believe that I have a right to divorce, or at least part of me feels justified at the thought of divorce.
9. I don't think I could ever live in the same house or love this person again.
10. I know that God said that we must forgive others for Him to forgive us, but right now the emotional pain seems to great to forgive.
11. I think that I love God more than I hate my spouse who betrayed me, but the thought of forgiving them seems impossible.
12. I want the best for my children, and for my own spiritual life, but I have endured so much already.

Truths about Divorce:

125

1. God hates it.
2. It permanently damages the children.
3. Most people who divorce wish that they had tried harder.
4. Children of divorce are more likely to divorce themselves.
5. Forgiveness is possible over time.
6. God will give super-natural help in rebuilding a marriage if His children ask him, and struggle to work through their pain and hurt.
7. The Devil wants you to go ahead and split your family.
8. The Devil wants you to constantly run anger, and vengeance through your mind.
9. Jesus knows how it feels to be betrayed and abandoned.
10. God knows all of your hurts and your feelings, and He cares deeply about you and your family.
11. The Great Physician can heal hurts that man cannot repair.
12. The Devil wants you to rush into a decision about divorce quickly while your feelings of anger, hate, and betrayal burn hot!
13. What you do now will effect your children's spiritual lives for eternity.
15. Children desperately need both a mom and a dad to help them grow up.

Divorce and Custody Effects on the Kids

1. Love your child enough to say no---this teaches them to "choose to be happy 20 yrs in the future" (don't train kids that they have to always have their own way to be happy)
2. Most couples use the kid as a weapon to punish their "ex"
3. Couples compete for the kid's love by giving more toys, etc....this damages the kid
4. Kids know how to manipulate: by whining. They make you feel guilty by reminding you that you messed up their life by divorcing their dad...
5. You give your kids things, and always say yes to:
   a. Punish your ex by getting your kid to love you more and them less
   b. You train your kid to believe that, "I have to get what I want to be happy." ...which damages his marriage 20 years in advance
6. Both sides are "using the kid" to advance their selfish agenda:
   a. Gifts are not for the kids good, but to meet the parent's emotional needs
   b. I want to hurt my "ex" by causing them to loose respect of others: including our kids
7. You must "require" that your kid respect and honor your ex, or they will rebel (they will go against you to honor their bio/absent parent who is under attack)
8. If you require them to respect your ex, only then are they free to love and respect their step-parent.
9. Parents who use their kids to punish their ex, force their kids into an impossible and "uncomfortable choice:" to not love one of their parents.
10. You are not really trying to help your kid, you are trying to meet your own needs (sexual, emotional)
11. ***Rip out your kids heart in an effort to heal your own heart, and fulfill your own selfish sexual and emotional desires.
12. You will not be able to get on with your life until you stop punishing the people in your present for what people in your past did or did not do to you or for you!
13. You are having to fight for your children's love now because you didn't put your spouse first ahead of your children in the past.
14. Stop trying to live through your children, and deal with your own issues and hurts from the past

Joe Brumfield   Jan 2009

<u>Therapy: How To Pretend You Don't Want to Get a Divorce When You Really Want one</u>   (How to Pretend that You <u>Want To Stay Married)</u>

1. Go to enough therapy sessions to make it look like you tried really tried.
2. Talk about how far your spouse has pushed you, and how much you have been wronged.
3. Tell how much you have put up with, and how good you have been.
4. Convince your parents that staying together and fighting is the worst thing for your kids.
5. Convince your kids that divorce is the best thing for them, and that their parents will fight less.
6. Pretend that you have no other possible lover waiting...even if you do.
7. Keep your options open while acting stressed and hurt.
8. Pretend that your spouse shouldn't be as hurt so you won't feel too guilty.
9. Ignore the facts about the lifetime negative effects of divorce on your kids.
10. Buy things for your spouse and kids, and try to look generous...
11. Say often, that you must_____ or life's pressures will destroy you. (put anything in the blank like spend money, have an affair, go on a Safari)
12. SATAN LOVES THIS KIND OF THINKING!!

Dr. Joe Brumfield

Dec 09

125c

1. Most people are pretending to be better than they are. They are lying in order to protect themselves from rejection.
2. Satan wants you to hide your sins, hurts and imperfections.
3. Satan wants you to believe that sharing your real self will cause you to be rejected and shamed.
4. Everyone is doing what they believe will help them feel loved. Their actions "make sense" to them!
5. Just because someone loves you, does not guarantee that you will feel loved.
6. If a person doesn't feel loved and valued by family, friends, spouse, etc., then they will not care much about grades, jobs, and activities.
7. People who misbehave are merely on a misguided search for the love that they don't feel inside.
8. Dating can fill the heart of someone who does not feel loved, but after marriage, these deep needs again rise to the surface.
9. People tend to marry someone who seems to fill the empty spot they have in their heart—someone who makes them feel loved.
10. Dating couples marry assuming that the love need now being filled by their date will carry over if they get married.
11. When the illusion that "we have an intimate loving relationship" fades, many people jump ship. They assume that the cause of not feeling loved is with their spouse rather than being with them.
12. If you depend on the person that you date or marry to "make you happy," you are on a crash course with disappointment!!
13. Our culture and our schools have accidentally but efficiently trained us to be extremely selfish and self-focused.
14. A focus on "what makes me happy" is the beginning of relationship cancer!

What People Actually Fear
(Regardless of their façade)

1. dying
2. being unloved
3. being disrespected
4. being unwanted
5. being exposed for what we really are
6. being inadequate
7. losing a loved one
8. losing a source of love or respect
9. debilitating illness
10. never finding a spouse
11. never being wanted as a spouse
12. being trapped in an unfulfilling marriage
13. failing at marriage
14. not finding a job
15. getting fired
16. being unable to care for their family
17. being abandoned
18. being betrayed
19. being unaccepted
20. going to Hell
21. getting caught by God
22. knowing the truth about themselves
23. admitting wrong
24. being wrong
25. suffering
26. being along
27. wasting one's life
28. there is no God
29. there is a God
30. not having enough money
31. not being take care of
32. going to a nursing home
33. being a "nothing"
34. having no purpose
35. that God is watching
36. that their secret sins are known

Dr. Joe Brumfield Nov 15, 2009

127

THERAPY QUESTIONS TO CONSIDER OR ASK
DR. JOE BRUMFIELD
NOV. 1997

1. Why are you here?
2. What would be a sign that things are improving?
3. When were things worse?
4. When better?
5. What was happening?
6. When was the problem not happening?
7. What would things look like if _____ wasn't happening?
8. What is your role in what's happening?
9. What would your _____ say you need to do?
10. What have you tried?
11. What worked (why)?
12. What did not work?
13. What good things are happening as a result of this problem?
14. Is your # 1 goal today the same as it was last week?
15. What has changed since before?
16. Why did the problem happen today instead of earlier?
17. What have you been doing over and over that has ben getting these same negative results over and over?
18. How are you continuing the problem?
19. If the problem was to go away or be resolved, what other (smaller) problems might crop up?
20. What do you want from me?
21. How are you doing?
22. What changed?
23. What do you want to stay the same?
24. What will it cost you to get rid of this problem?

128

25. How have other people effected your problem?
26. Who is benefiting from this problem?
27. Why is this not your fault?
28. What part of this is your fault?
29. What can/cannot be changed about this situation?
30. What are you doing right?
31. How hard are you willing to work on this?
32. How much are you willing to sacrifice, pay, give, give up to fix this?
33. What else? Like what? How is that?
34. "What was that like for you?"
35. I see the surface problem-What do you think the real (root) problem is?
36. What would happen if you did that...?
37. When this problem is solved, what will you be doing and thinking differently?

Counseling Ideas for a Non-Christian Couple

129

1. Get to know them/small talk
2. Collect Information about family backgrounds
3. Ask them what they think the other partner wants them to change
4. Consider using the miracle question
5. Explain to them the difference in dealing with Christian couples
6. Educate them regarding Christian Commitment and Trust
7. Let them know what you want for them
8. Explain how they have brought hurts, insecurities, and unmet needs from their families in the past.
9. Give some examples of how family baggage comes into a relationship and causes problems.
10. Assist the couple in sorting out specific issues brought from the past
11. Ask the couple if they mind if you pray for them
12. Be honest with the couple in telling them you long for them to have a relationship where they treat each other right when one doesn't feel like it, and the other doesn't deserve it.
13. Suggest some helpful books for them to read: The Bible, His Needs, Her Needs, etc.
14. Explain the benefits of following your assignments

Questions to ask at some point:
1. What was it like when things were good?
2. Why did you fall in love with them in the first place?
3. How are they similar to your parent of the same gender?
4. How do you treat them that is related to how your parent's treated you?
5. What kind of a miracle would have to happen for things to be a whole lot better?
6. Tell me your dream for the future if things work out.
7. How important do you wish that God would be in your relationship?
8. Do you know what happens to couples who read the Bible?
9. What would you like me to do to help you?
10. What behaviors does your partner wish you would stop or change?
11. What made it hard for you to come today?
12. How hard are you willing to work to save this relationship?
13. If God were standing here, what would He tell you to do?

Dr. Joe Brumfield

130

Helping Fighting Couples In Early Sessions (and late)
**Allow the Anesthetic (hope) to take effect before beginning painful surgery

1. Compliment them for coming: "A sign of seriousness—and a predictor of success"
2. If they are religious,--Ask them what God wants to happen with their marriage.
3. How might God be willing to help?
4. What were your dreams of marriage when dating?
5. What are some of his/her good points that attracted you in the beginning?
6. What are some bad things that you are saying or doing that you think that God would want you to stop?
7. How badly do you want to please God?
8. What do you believe will be the consequences if you go against God?
9. Are you hinting at divorce because you really want one, or because you desperately want your marriage to be better?
10. What does the Devil want you to do with this marriage?
11. What things does the Devil want you to say when you are upset are frustrated?
12. Do you believe that God cares deeply about your marriage?   Do you believe God has the power to help?   Do you believe He wants to and is willing to help?
13. How could you get God to help you build the marriage you want?
14. What lies does the Devil want you to believe that will discourage you about your future together?
15. Which lies has the Devil been most successful with?
Dr. Joe Brumfield Oct 10, 2001

131

WRITING YOUR OWN EULOGY
(*As you hope it will be*)

1. **Eulogies from Co-workers:**

   a. How he/she worked

   b. Attitudes

   c. Special things said

   d. Spiritual things

   e. Evangelism matters

   f. Special things done

   g. Other

2. **Eulogies from Church Members:**

   a. Encouragement

   b. Service

   c. Teaching

   d. Faithfulness

   e. Example

   f. Other

3. **Eulogies from Family Members:**

   a. Spouse

   b. Parents or Children

   c. Brothers or Sisters

132

HOW DO YOU SPEND YOUR TIME?

-How people spend their time (avg. lifetime)

    20 years and one month working

    6 ½ years eating

    10 years and 5 months (recreation type

    activity)

    6 ½ years driving

    4 years being sick

    2 years and 4 months getting dressed

    9-12 ½ years watching television

        (82,195 to 109,500 hours)

    1.2 years listening to music just between 7th and 12th grades(10,500 hours)

    1.4 years in the classroom K-12

Psalms 90:12 Teach us to number our days so we may apply our hearts to wisdom.

Eph. 5:15-16 Be very careful then, how you live...making the most of every opportunity...(Redeeming the time, for the days are evil)

    (KJV)

What if Spiritual Things Add Up Like Physical Things?

Little things can add up to a huge price!!

Approximately 600 calories are burned for every hour of calisthenics done by a 155-pound person. 600 Calories burned per hour = 10 Calories burned for 60 seconds of calisthenics. If you burn 10 Calories for every minute of jumping jacks, and there are 5 Calories in 1 jellybean, that = 0.5 minutes.
You need to do about 30 jumping jacks to burn the calories from 1 small jellybean.

Is it worth the price? Feeding yourself empty fat calories comes at a great cost!
Feeding yourself negative spiritual food comes at even greater cost. God promises that we will reap what we sow!

If it takes three hours of walking to burn off a hamburger, coke and French fries, do you still want them?   If a large fast food hamburger with cheese is 760 Calories, and   If 30 jumping jacks burns 5 calories,   How many jumping jacks will you have to pay for "pigging out?"

if 30 jumping jacks burn 5 calories so 6 jumping jacks burn one calorie, then it takes 4560 jumping jacks to undo one whopper with cheese.

209 mins of walking =86 mins of jogging =63 mins of swimming =115 mins of cycling

What Are Your Negative Spiritual Calories?

What Is Your Positive Spiritual Exercise?

Dr Joe Brumfield December 2010

Rate Yourself on the extent to which Jesus Is Lord in the following areas.
One is low and ten is high

	Jesus is Not Lord	Jesus Is Lord
How I use my time	1—2—3—4—5—6—7—8—9—10	
My Thoughts at work	1—2—3—4—5—6—7—8—9—10	
My words in public	1—2—3—4—5—6—7—8—9—10	
My words in private	1—2—3—4—5—6—7—8—9—10	
My prayer life	1—2—3—4—5—6—7—8—9—10	
How I spend money	1—2—3—4—5—6—7—8—9—10	
How much I think about other's feelings	1—2—3—4—5—6—7—8—9—10	
Who I talk to at the church building	1—2—3—4—5—6—7—8—9—10	
What movies and television I watch	1—2—3—4—5—6—7—8—9—10	
What movies and tv I want to watch	1—2—3—4—5—6—7—8—9—10	
How I view other people	1—2—3—4—5—6—7—8—9—10	
How well I control my anger	1—2—3—4—5—6—7—8—9—10	
How much I encourage other people	1—2—3—4—5—6—7—8—9—10	
What I do in my spare time	1—2—3—4—5—6—7—8—9—10	
What I channel surf to see	1—2—3—4—5—6—7—8—9—10	
What clothes I wear	1—2—3—4—5—6—7—8—9—10	
How I keep my house and car	1—2—3—4—5—6—7—8—9—10	
How I treat my body	1—2—3—4—5—6—7—8—9—10	
How many treasures I store up in heaven	1—2—3—4—5—6—7—8—9—10	
How many treasures I store up on earth	1—2—3—4—5—6—7—8—9—10	
How I treat my children/parents	1—2—3—4—5—6—7—8—9—10	
What I think about other people	1—2—3—4—5—6—7—8—9—10	
How I act when I am tired or frustrated	1—2—3—4—5—6—7—8—9—10	
How I drive	1—2—3—4—5—6—7—8—9—10	
What I think or say about other's driving	1—2—3—4—5—6—7—8—9—10	
What I do when no one is looking	1—2—3—4—5—6—7—8—9—10	
How I deal with my own mistakes	1—2—3—4—5—6—7—8—9—10	
How I deal with frustrations	1—2—3—4—5—6—7—8—9—10	
How I deal with hurtful people	1—2—3—4—5—6—7—8—9—10	
How I deal with people in business	1—2—3—4—5—6—7—8—9—10	
What music I listen to	1—2—3—4—5—6—7—8—9—10	
How I use up my energy	1—2—3—4—5—6—7—8—9—10	
What I eat	1—2—3—4—5—6—7—8—9—10	
My general attitude	1—2—3—4—5—6—7—8—9—10	
My conscious efforts to reach the lost	1—2—3—4—5—6—7—8—9—10	

"If Jesus is not Lord of all, Jesus is not Lord at all!"

134

How Do I Take My Negative Thoughts Captive?

2 Cor 10:4-5   Paul said that Christians can break down the strongholds of Satan by taking every thought captive, and making them obedient to Christ
1. Consciously choosing your thoughts is the key to winning.
      a. Pro 23:7 A man becomes what he thinks about in his
          heat.
      b. Php 4:8 Christians are commanded to think about
          things that are true, noble, praiseworthy, etc.

Several helpful facts from DR. CAROLINE LEAF'S BOOK: <u>WHO SWITCHED OFF MY BRAIN</u>:

2. Our brain's have around 100 trillion brain cells (neurons) according to some scientists. On each neuron we have the capacity for 70,000 "branches" (dendrites) We will never use our full capacity of memory storage.

3. Negative thinking actually shrivels up little branches (dendrites) You can actually see the damage in brain scan pictures. Anger, hate, bitterness, etc actually causes brain damage that spreads in your brain.

4. Positive and happy thoughts and memories look very different as they effect the human brain!

      a. When you have negative thoughts a real physical change
          occurs in your brain
- **This effects the electrical/chemical feedback loop in your brain and causes changes in your whole body**
- **The middle part of your brain transfers your thought into an actual physical reaction in your body**
- **TOXIC THINKING IN YOUR BRAIN ACTUALLY BECOMES A PHYSICAL REACTION IN YOUR BODY**

135

Satan's Lies That I have Believed

Select the lies you have used on yourself and talk about the wounds you have received in the past that helped you believe them?
Eph 6:10-18, 2 Cor 11:3, 1 Jn 5:19, 2 Cor 4:4, Jn 12:42-43, Jn 5:39-44
(You will be spiritually and emotionally crippled if Satan can get you to keep telling yourself these lies)

1. This is just the way I am, I can't change---its too late.
2. My problems are all because my family was messed up.
3. I can be happy if certain people like and accept me.
4. Everything has be fair or my life seems ruined.
5. It doesn't feel like God really cares about me.
6. Strong men (or women) don't show emotion.
7. Strong men (or women) don't ask for help-I don't need anybody.
8. I would be proven weak if I ever admit weakness or faults.
9. Things have to go my way for me to be happy.
10. I can't forgive people who don't ask or don't deserve it.
11. Nobody loves me, why should they? I feel worthless and unlovable.
12. If It's OK with everybody else it seems right for me.
13. I can work hard enough to prove or earn my value.
14. I have to do everything perfect or no one will accept me.
15. Getting things I want will make life enjoyable.
16. If I don't feel forgiven, I must not be forgiven.
17. I can't make it -even with God's help -my life feels ruined.
18. It is too late for me to change. Too much damage has been
19. I'll never be able to change what I think, or feel, or want.
20. My childhood will always have a negative effect on me.
21. God can't or won't forgive my past—its my fault so why try.
22. If people really knew me, I doubt if they would like me.
23 It feels like everyone is against me –it feels so unfair
24. I'll always be a failure because I've always felt like a failure.
25 If only _____ hadn't happened, then I could be happy.

Joe Brumfield 1998 revised April 2002

136

SCRIPTURAL PRINCIPLES THAT COUNTER MYTHICAL THINKING
Dr. Brumfield

John 8:32 ...the truth shall set you free
Romans 8:28...in all things God works for the good of those that
Philippians 4:8 ...whatever things are good, pure, lovely...think
    on these things
John 3 Nicodemus and the new birth (a new start)
John 4 Woman at the well with 5 marriages behind her, and now
    living with a man...Jesus offers her living water (there
    is hope for all of us)
1 John 1:9 If we confess our sins, God will forgive us
Luke 15 Prodigal son (God is waiting and longing to forgive)
1 Corinthians 10:13 ...no temptation more than we can stand--
    with every temptation, God will make a way of escape..
James 1:2-6 Be joyful in trials because they teach you patience
    and can lead to spiritual maturity
James 5:16 Confess your sins one to another and pray for each other
Proverbs 28:13 One who confesses and renounces his sins finds mercy
    --one who conceals his sins does not prosper
Eph 4:25-27 Don't let the sun go down while you are angry--or
    you'll give the devil a foothold
1 Peter 5:6-7 Cast all of your anxieties on him because he cares
    for you
Matt 5-7 Follow the law + the heart of the law
Matt 18:15-19 If your brother sins against you-go to him/2 or 3
Matt 23:25-26 Clean the inside first--then the outside will be
Philippians 4:6 Don't worry-tell God--He will give you peace

IRRATIONAL BELIEFS PUSHED BY THE DEVIL:
1. It's too late for me
2. I'm trapped by the past
3. It's not my fault-or it's all my fault
4. I can make it on my own
5. People and things make me mad
6. that's just the way I am--I can't change
7. things can make me happy
8. God would never forgive me
9. It's God's fault
10. There is a magical answer to my problem
11. I'm the only one with problems like this
12. My looks are everything
13. Divorce is O.K.
14. The world's standards = OKness
15. Nobody cares about me

COMMON PROBLEMS BROUGHT INTO THERAPY
1. defiance
2. affairs
3. abuse: physical, substance, children, emotional, verbal
4. depression
5. anxiety
6. bed wetting
7. hopelessness
8. guilt
9. Divorce mediation
10. lack of belief-faith
11. Attachment
12. anger
13. violence
14. Adultery/Fornication
15. Relationship problem
16. Loneliness
17. Parenting
18. Homosexuality
19. Self-esteem
20. Grief
21. Addictions
22. Pregnancy/Marriage

137

The Devil's Power

1. Satan has to ask God's permission to try you. Job 1-3
2. God always limits Satan--you will never be tempted beyond what you can stand. 1 Cor. 10:13
3. God always gives a way of escape when one is tempted. 1 Cor. 10:13 God doesn't tempt anyone. 1 Cor. 10:13
4. Don't slander the Devil-the angel would not. Jude 8-10
5. Don't give the Devil too much credit.
Each one is tempted when they are drawn away by their own lust. James 1:13
6. He incited David to take a census. 1 Chron. 21:1
7. He kept a woman bound with illness for 18 yrs. Lk 13:16
8. He asked to sift Peter like wheat. Lk 22:31
9. He prompted Judas to betray Jesus. Jn 13:2
10. He entered Judas. Jn. 13:27
11. He filled the hearts of Ananias and Sapphira. Acts 5:3
12. He blinds the minds of unbelievers. 2 Cor. 4:4
13. He is the ruler of the kingdom of the air.
14. He is at work in those who are disobedient.
15. He can take people captive to do his will. 2 Tim 2:26
16. Satan's workers killed Job's kids. Job 1:19
17. Satan used a mighty wind to collapse a roof.
18. Satan used nature to kill children, servants and flocks. Job 1-3
19. Satan uses armies to do his will. (Chaldean raiding party) Job 1-3
20. Satan can use your friends to discourage you with false teaching and bad advice. (Job's friends)
21. Satan used Job's wife to encourage him to curse God and die.

22. Demons are not the same as Idols 1 Cor 10:19-22
23. Demons are evil, and do exist.
24. Stay away from demons--God is jealous.
25. Demons influence our world.
26. The sphere of demon's work is unclear.
27. Victory over Satan is guaranteed to the faithful who keep their armor on.
28. False teachers and false doctrine are taught by demons
29. Greater is He that is in you, than he that is in the world.
30. Don't mess with the occult or you will be in company with demonic influence.
31. Satan, or the Devil is the God of this age 2 Cor 4:4
32. Satan is the "prince of this world" Jn 14:30 & 16:11
33. Satan has blinded the minds of unbelievers so that they cannot see the light of the gospel of the glory of Christ 2 Cor. 4:4
34. Some (or all) who oppose the gospel have fallen into a trap of the devil "who has taken them captive to do his will 2 Tim 2:26
35. Satan holds people in slavery under the basic principles of this world Gal 4:3
36. Satan is the ruler of the kingdom of the air Eph 2:1-2
37. Satan has schemes to take advantage of Christians 2 Cor. 2:11; Eph. 6:11
38. Satan often presents himself in a positive light to further his deceitful work 2 Cor 11:14
39. Idols have no real existence 1 Cor 8:4
40. 1 Kings 22:19-38 Spirits meet with God to discuss leading wicked king Ahab to his death in battle.
41. The spirit is a lying spirit in the mouth of Ahab's prophets to lead Ahab into an ill advised battle.
42. An arrow shot at random "just happens"??? to hit disguised King Ahab between the joints of his armor.

139

Commands of Jesus

Just before ascending to Heaven Jesus gave final instructions to his disciples. He told them to go into all the world and make disciples. They were to baptize these disciples and then teach the baptized disciples to obey what Jesus had commanded(Matt. 28:18-20). Have you been practicing Jesus direct and clear commands as much as other seemingly important things? Rate yourself in the practice or the teaching of the following commands of Jesus. Use a one to ten scale. One is extremely low or rare for practice or teaching. Ten is extremely high or frequent for practice or teaching. Rate yourself first on Personal practice, then rate your teaching and preaching practice. You may use any number from one to ten:

___Let your light shine before men so they can see your good deeds and praise your
    Father who is in heaven (Matt. 5:16)

___Go and be reconciled to your brother(anyone who has something against you)
    before trying to worship God (Matt. 5:24)

___Settle matters quickly with your adversary (Matt. 5:25)

___If your right hand or right eye(even something very important to you) causes you
    to sin, cut it off/gouge it out and throw it away. It is better to lose part of your
    body than to have your whole body thrown into hell. (Matt. 5:27-30)

___Do not swear at all...simply let your yes be yes, and your no be no. Anything
    beyond this comes from the evil one (Matt. 5:34-37)

___Do not resist an evil person...turn the other cheek (Matt. 5:39)

___If someone wants to sue you for your coat, let him have your shirt also (Mt. 5:40)

___Do twice as much as you are required to do (Go the second mile)(Matt. 5:41)

___Do not turn away from someone who wants to borrow from you (Matt. 5:42)

___Love your enemies and pray for those who persecute you (Matt. 5:43-48)

___Be perfect as your Heavenly Father is perfect (Matt.5:48)

___Be careful to not do your acts of righteousness (Praying, Fasting, Giving)
    before men to be seen by them (Matt. 6:1-18)

___Do your acts of righteousness in secret (Praying, Fasting, Giving) Matt. 6:1-18)

___Do not pray like pagans who think they will be heard because of their many
    words (Matt. 6:7-8)

___Pray like Jesus prayed: "Our Father who art in heaven..." (Matt. 6:9-13)

___Do not store up treasures for yourself on earth (because your heart will
    be where your treasure is) (Matt. 6:19-21)

___Do store up treasures for yourself in Heaven (Matt. 6:19-21)

___Do not worry about your life: what you will eat, drink, or wear (Matt. 6:25-32)

___Do not judge because you will be judged with the measure you use on others
    (Matt. 7:1-5)

___Get rid of the plank in your eye so you can see clearly to remove the speck that
    is in your brother's eye (Matt. 7:3-5)

___Do not give dogs what is sacred, or throw your pearls to hogs (Matt. 7:6)

___Ask and it will be given to you,   ___Seek and you will find,

___Knock, and the door will be opened to you (Matt 7:1-12)

___Do to others what you would like them to do to you (Matt. 7:12)

___Enter through the narrow/straight gate because it is the road to life and only
    a few find it--Many find the broad road to destruction (Matt. 7: 13-14)

___Watch out for false prophets--they come in sheep's clothes (Matt. 7:15-20)

Dr. Joe Brumfield January 25, 2000

Commands of Jesus Study Questions

1. Should Christians give more emphasis to the specific commands of Jesus than to traditions, beliefs and practices not specifically commanded by Jesus?   Why?

2. What types of things did Jesus give commands about?

3. What types of things did Jesus seem to give few or no commands about?

4. Which commands from the list have you heard the most teaching about?

5. Which commands from the list have you heard the least teaching about?

6. Which one command would be of great help to your family?

7. Which one command do you personally need to work on more? Explain:

Single Sentences to Bring God Into Brief Conversations

(The One Thing I Will Ask You Before Eternity)

Joe Brumfield Feb 15, 2008

Rationale: Most human interactions will be brief: store clerk, passing on the sidewalk, waiting in the checkout line, elevator trip.   How can you plant the seed?

1. Pray for these people-before you meet them, and after you meet them.   Remember what the Apostle Paul said: "the god of this age has blinded them so that they cannot see the glory of the gospel...

2. Ask them about things from which they get emotional value: their kids, family, job. Keep a record of their name and any thing you remember—family, job, problems, conversations

3. One shot statements:
    a. What do you want said at your funeral
    b. Non religious historians agree that Jesus Christ was a real person in History who was crucified. What do you think is true?

4.   Why do you think that those who claimed to see him alive after his death refused to recant (change their story) even when threatened with torture and death?

5. Where will you be when you get where you are going?

6. Why do you think Jesus Christ has influenced history more than all kings and rulers put together (as claimed by many scholars)?

7. How long do you think you will live after you retire?   And then What?   And then What.......repeat...

8. Are you moving toward your treasures or away from them? Do you think it is possible to store up treasures in heaven?

9. Why do you think many of the rich and famous people are some of the most unhappy people on earth?

Single Sentences To Bring God Into Brief Conversations

10. Why do you think God would love and forgive a sinner like me? He has blessed me in so many ways (tell one---ex: He has rescued my wife from cancer)   It is interesting that bringing cancer into the conversation connects with almost everyone.   Everyone has some family member or friend effected by cancer.

11. Why do you think (people like to have their opinions valued) so many people waste their lives collecting stuff that won't fit in their casket?

12. What do you think happens to people when they die?   Do you think that what the Bible says about Heaven is true?

13. I read in the Bible about many finding destruction and few finding life (heaven)   Do you think Jesus really meant what He said?

14. Do you think the sun is going to come up again tomorrow? God sure is good to us.

15. Why did my students laugh at me when I held up my watch and said, "this watch happened by accident!   Nobody made it"????   Their High School science teacher told them that the world is an accident.

16. Didn't God make a beautiful sunrise today?

17. Do you thing Jesus was a liar who claimed to be the son of God, a nutcase who thought he was, or was he really who he claimed to be. (scholars agree that he was a real person in history)?

18. Do you think people are happier if they reach the top rung of the social ladder, or if they find something beyond self to live for?

19. What would you recommend for a church that doesn't want to be a social club, or a meeting of show off religious people, but just wants to be honest followers of Jesus?

20. Why do you think church sometimes drive people away from God?

21. I am a preacher who is a sinner. (forgiven) I am a hypocrite sometimes. (selfish, anger, grouchy at home sometimes, but nice at church) What do you think I should preach about next Sunday? You know people.   What do people need?

Single Sentences To Bring God Into Brief Conversations

22. What would they have to do to change and draw people to God?

23. World class scholars (list some) say that there is more evidence that Jesus was a real person than there is for Plato, or Aristotle, etc. What do you think?

24. I believe that Jesus was real....lived and died....and rose from the dead. Sometimes I live for him, and sometimes I struggle with living for myself instead. Do you think I should give up on what is true because I am an imperfect follower?

25. What in the world is holding the stars in place?

26. How in the world do you think the Old Testament predicted so many details about Jesus hundreds of years before He was born?

27. (For former church attenders/unchurched) Why do you think some people quit going to church?

28. Why do you think people quit on God because "church people" are sometimes fake?

29. Ask for advice about being a better Christian. Tell why you believe in Jesus, and then admit some of your failures. Tell how God continually forgives you, and then ask for advice on forgiving yourself?

30. Explain how you are overwhelmed by God's free gift of forgiveness, and ask for advice about not trying to "earn your way."

31. I need a shirt that says, "Was Jesus a liar, the Lord, or a Lunatic? (That could lead into some interesting conversations) I believe I heard Josh McDowell ask this question.

32. How about a shirt that says "From the goo, to the zoo, to you" Are we really an accident? I think I heard that phrase from Frank Peretti

33. How many more years do you think you'll live?

34. When leaving the check out counter say, "God bless you." If they say, God bless you too, say, He has!! He is healing my wife from cancer....or tell what God has done for you.

141

Decision Making Principles for the Christian

Hebrews 5:14 But solid food is for the mature, who by constant use have trained themselves to distinguish good from evil.

Before you decide, ask yourselves the following questions?

1. **Is it Biblical?**
   Does scripture give a <u>specific</u> answer either for or against?
2. **Would Jesus do it?**
   If he wouldn't, then you shouldn't either.
   We Christians no longer live, but Christ lives in us Gal 2:20
3. **Will it bring Glory to God?**
   Whatever you do, do it <u>all for the glory of God</u> 1 Cor. 10:31
4. **Can it be done in the name of the Lord Jesus?**
   Whatever you do in word or deed, do it all in the name of the Lord Jesus Col. 3:17
5. **Is it coming from selfish or unselfish motives?**
   God will expose men's motives 1 Cor. 4:5; Some prayers Don't receive because people ask with the wrong motives James 4:3
6. **Have I prayed seriously about it?**
   1 Thes. 5:17 Pray without ceasing; The prayer of a righteous man is powerful James 5:15-16
7. **Is it a righteous use of my time?**
   Use your time wisely (Redeem it) Because the days are evil Eph. 5:16; work while it is day, the night comes when no one can work Jn 9:4
8. **Do I have any doubts about this?** If you have doubts and you do it anyway, you are condemned Rom 14:23; Everything that does not come from your faith is sin!
9. **Will this cause anyone to stumble?**
   Do not cause anyone to stumble Rom. 14:20; 1 Cor 10:32
   If you cause one of these little ones to stumble... Matt 18:6

142

10. Will it cause me or anyone else to think about anything that
    is not pure, lovely and excellent?
    Think on these things Philippians 4:8

11. Does it appear or "seem" to be evil? 1 Thess. 5:22
    Flee the very appearance of evil (Avoid every kind of evil)

12. Will it cause you to have anything to do with evil things?
    Have nothing to do with the unfruitful deeds of darkness
    but rather expose them Eph. 5:11

13. Is it constructive and beneficial?
    Just because something is permissible does not mean
    that it is beneficial. 1 Cor 10:23-24

14. Is it seeking your good or that of others?
    Nobody should seek his own good, but that of others
    1 Cor. 10:24

15. Is it a first priority matter for me as a Christian?
    Seek first the kingdom Matt 6:33

16. How will it effect the lost?
    1 Cor 9: 12-22 put up with anything rather than hinder the
    Gospel, become weak to win the weak, become a slave to win
    as many as possible, become all things to all men, so that by
    all possible means you might save some.

17. Does it help unbelievers understand about God and the Gospel?
    Worship activities should always consider this 1 Cor 14:24

18. Is this upbuilding to fellow Christians?
    Worship activities must build up the others 1 Cor 14

19. Am I doing the good that I know to do?
    Not doing the good you know is sin James 4:17

20. Is there a substitute for this that is better?

21. Have I examined all of the possibilities?

22. Have I sought the counsel of wise men?

23. Will it build unity in my family and the Church?

24. How will this effect myself, and my family in the future?

25. Will I be glad about this tomorrow or in the future?

26. Where will this possibly lead? Do I want to go there?

27. Does it hinder my doing the things God commanded,
    or nullify His Word?   Joe Brumfield, 1995

143

Decision Making Principles Study Questions

1. Which biblical Decision Making Principle is usually the most uncomfortable for you to follow?

3. What area do you believe most Christians are <u>least</u> likely to use God's principles for guiding them?

4. What extent do you believe that God actually expects us to put these tough principles into practice?

5. What underlying motive/s might cause a Christian to argue against using God's Decision Making Principles?

6. What lie, excuse or rationalization does the Devil hope <u>you</u> will believe that will hinder you from making Godly decisions

7. List 3 decisions that you made this week:
   (Decisions can be big or small: clothes to wear, movie to watch, ask someone out or not, take a nap or not, eat ice cream or not....etc)
   a.

   b.

   c.

8. List honestly the principles that you actually used in making the decisions. Were you conscious of these principles when you made your decision?

Marriage and Family Scriptures

New International Version 1984, ©1984 (NIV1984)

Gen 2:18 The LORD God said, "It is not good for the man to be alone. I will make a helper suitable for him."

Deuteronomy 4:9 [9] Only be careful, and watch yourselves closely so that you do not forget the things your eyes have seen or let them slip from your heart as long as you live. Teach them to your children and to their children after them.

Deuteronomy 6:4-9 [4] Hear, O Israel: The LORD our God, the LORD is one. [5] Love the LORD your God with all your heart and with all your soul and with all your strength. [6] These commandments that I give you today are to be upon your hearts. [7] Impress them on your children. Talk about them when you sit at home and when you walk along the road, when you lie down and when you get up. [8] Tie them as symbols on your hands and bind them on your foreheads. [9] Write them on the doorframes of your houses and on your gates.

Deuteronomy 24:1-4 [1] If a man marries a woman who becomes displeasing to him because he finds something indecent about her, and he writes her a certificate of divorce, gives it to her and sends her from his house, [2] and if after she leaves his house she becomes the wife of another man, [3] and her second husband dislikes her and writes her a certificate of divorce, gives it to her and sends her from his house, or if he dies, [4] then her first husband, who divorced her, is not allowed to marry her again after she has been defiled. That would be detestable in the eyes of the LORD. Do not bring sin upon the land the LORD your God is giving you as an inheritance.

Malachi 2:16 "I hate divorce," says the LORD God of Israel, "and I hate a man's covering himself with violence as well as with his garment," says the LORD Almighty.
So guard yourself in your spirit, and do not break faith.

Matthew 5:9 [9] Blessed are the peacemakers, for they will be called sons of God.

Matthew 5:23-24 [23] "Therefore, if you are offering your gift at the altar and there remember that your brother has something against you, [24] leave your gift there in front of the altar. First go and be reconciled to your brother; then come and offer your gift.

Matthew 5:27-29 [27] "You have heard that it was said, 'Do not commit adultery.' [28] But I tell you that anyone who looks at a woman lustfully has already committed adultery with her in his heart. [29] If your right eye causes you to sin, gouge it out and throw it away. It is better for you to lose one part of your body than for your whole body to be thrown into hell.

145

Marriage and Family Scriptures Study Questions

1. What should one's view be of their children after they are grown and have their own children?

2. Read the context of Malachi 2:16 and explain why God hates adultery and divorce so much, and yet loves adulterers and the divorced enough to send his son to be killed for their sins.

3. Why is it wrong to misuse people in your mind (sexually or any other way)?

4. Why is sleeping with a prostitute or anyone else you are not married to so offensive to God?

5. When does God specifically say that He allows divorce?

6. Why is it sometimes so difficult for us to accept what God says about divorce and remarriage?

7. What are 5 things that older women are to teach the younger:

146

8. Why do many people not want "be busy at home" to mean what they suspect it might mean?

9. If our own lifestyles did not prejudice us, what would "being busy at home" likely mean?

10. Why does God tell husbands that it is essential for them to share regular intimacy?

11. What are two commands God gave to children?

12. Explain God's method for dealing with a situation where a wife has become a Christian, but her husband has not.

13. What are 3 rules for husbands from God:

14. What are 3 rules for wives from God:

147

Counseling Scriptures

1. Proverbs 15:1 A soft (gentle) answer turns away wrath
2. James 5:16 Confess your sins one to another
3. Philippians 3:13 Forget the past and strain toward the future
4. Matthew 6:34 Do not worry about tomorrow--each day has enough trouble of its own
5. Matthew 5:23-24 Go and be reconciled to your brother before you Offer your gift to God
6. Ephesians 4:29 Speak only what is helpful for building others up according to their needs
7. Philippians 4:6-7 Do not be anxious about anything--but by prayer and thanksgiving present your requests to God...and God will give you peace
8. Philippians 4:8 Think only on true, noble, right, pure, lovely, excellent things
9. Proverbs 16:32 A patient man who controls his temper is better than one who takes a city
10. John 8:32 The truth shall set you free
11. Romans 8:28 in all things God works for the good of those who love Him and are called according to His purpose
12. 1 John 1:9 If we confess our sins, God is faithful and will forgive us
13. Luke 15 (Prodigal son) God is waiting and longing for the sinner to come home
14. Matthew 23:25-26 Clean the inside first, and then the outside will be clean
15. Matthew 18:15-19 If your brother sins, go to him, just between the two of you
16. 1 Peter 5:6-7 Cast all of your anxieties on Him, because He cares for you
17. Ephesians 4:25-27 Don't let the sun go down while you're angry... Or you will give the devil a foothold
18. James 1:2-6 Be joyful in trials, because they teach you patience, and can lead you toward spiritual maturity
19. Proverbs 28:13 One who confesses and renounces his sins find mercy, --one who conceals his sins does not prosper

Brumfield handout/ March 1999

Who Says that God Cares About Emotional Closeness?
"I don't care if your kids are grown and your grandkids are 25 and on drugs, it is never to late to build relationships."   ---Emotional closeness is inherent in all spiritual relationships

1. **Romans 12:10**
   Be devoted to one another in brotherly love. Honor one another above yourselves.—write a letter and tell them you will always be there for them no matter what
2. **1 John 4:12**
   No one has ever seen God; but if we love one another, God lives in us and his love is made complete in us.—show how much you love a church member who irritates and frustrates you
3. **2 Corinthians 13:12**
   Greet one another with a holy kiss.—Hug everybody
   Ephesians 5:21
   Submit to one another out of reverence for Christ. Model yielding your favorite ice cream, your restaurant choice, the remote, going shopping
   1 Peter 4:9
   Offer hospitality to one another without grumbling.—old goat for supper
4. **John 13:35**
   By this all men will know that you are my disciples, if you love one another."—some people must use buildings, signs, and yellow page ads
5. **1 Corinthians 6:6**
   But instead, one brother goes to law against another—and this in front of unbelievers!let your brother take you---for the sake of Jesus
   Ephesians 4:2
   Be completely humble and gentle; be patient, bearing with one another in love. How many chances do your kids say you will give a brother
   1 Thessalonians 5:11
   Therefore encourage one another and build each other up, just as in fact you are doing. Speak only what builds others up—what % positive?
6. **Ephesians 4:32**
   Be kind and compassionate to one another, forgiving each other, just as in Christ God forgave you. Talk about the extent of forgiving the undeserving
7. **1 Peter 5:14**
   Greet one another with a kiss of love. Peace to all of you who are in Christ. Loving-non-sexual touch is essential
8. **1 John 4:11**
   Dear friends, since God so loved us, we also ought to love one another.—loving each other is the natural response of being loved by God
   1 John 3:11
   [*Love one another*] This is the message you heard from the beginning: We should love one another. –Why is this the main message?
9. **John 13:34**
   "A new command I give you: Love one another. As I have loved you, so you must love one another.

148

WHAT THE BIBLE SAYS ABOUT HOW TO TREAT YOUR SPOUSE

1. Gal. 6:2 Bear one another's burdens...
2. Rom. 14: 19 let us pursue...the building up of one another...
3. 1Thess. 5: 15 Seek after that which is good for one another
4. 1Thess. 5: 11 Therefore encourage one another, and build one another up, just as you also are doing...
5. Heb. 10:24 Let us consider how to stimulate one another to love and good deeds...
6. Matt. 7: 12 Whatever you want others to do for you, do to them, for this is the Law and the Prophets
7. 1Cor. 13:4-8 (Love is actions not merely feelings) love is patient, love is kind...keeps no record of wrongs..
8. Heb. 3:13 Encourage one another day after day...lest any of you be hardened by the deceitfulness of sin...
9. Eph. 4:32 Be ye kind one to another, tender hearted, forgiving one another, even as God for Christ's sake hath forgiven you.

Dr. Joe Brumfield
Harding University

With Whom Will You Worship/Assemble/Eat/ Fellowship?
(Yanking the weeds out of "our" wheat field)

**Is the word worship ever used in connection with the Lord's Day assembly of Christians? If the word "worship" is used outside of the assembly 99 % of the time in the New Testament how does this effect "worship" discussions?

Must you decide who is a "real Christian" to associate or not associate with them? Why does Paul say not to associate with an immoral, etc. person who <u>claims</u> to be a brother?

Can you "sit in church," "Fellowship" or "associate" with someone who:

   a. takes the Lord's supper twice on Sunday?
   b. claims to be a spiritual leader, but is not considerate of his spouse? (1 Peter 3-7+)
   c. hates another Christian because of a bad business deal?
   d. passes the Lord's Supper and then goes home and watches "R rated programming?"
   e. sings Fanny J. Crosby songs, but refuses to read Max Lucado's books?
   f. grounds their kids for cheating on a math test, but uses a radar detector in their car.
   g. binds rules like: "Anything not expressly authorized in the Bible is forbidden"---on music, but not on church buildings?
   h. takes the Lord's supper on Thursday "on the night He was betrayed" after the example of Jesus, but not on Sunday after the example of Paul?
   i. makes their kids go to bed early on a "school night" but lets them stay up late on Saturday night?
   j. makes their kids eat vegetables and brush their teeth, but lets them consume any movie or music they wish?
   k. leads "holy" prayers on Sunday, but only "says grace" at home?
   l. requires doctrinal orthodoxy of "other" religious people to accept and love them, but does not require their own children to pray and study with the family daily at home?

m. fights for "the correct view" of the thousand year reign, but doesn't fight for "visiting people in prison" or feeding the hungry?

n. makes disciples, baptizes them, than teaches them to obey Jesus commands plus examples and inferences

o. is baptized for forgiveness of sins but not to receive the gift of the Holy Spirit?

p. Raises hands when he prays?

q. Asks elders to anoint him or her with oil and pray?

r. Honors (for the things they have right) and listens to powerful preachers preach about Jesus (preachers who do not know about baptism to receive the gift of the Spirit)—instead of writing them up in the Jerusalem Times?

s. uses Strong's concordance, but will not listen to Billy Graham.

t. Spends more on hobbies and entertainment than they give to the poor

u. condemns denominational mission efforts but has not told their own next door neighbor about Jesus

v. thinks they have a monopoly on salvation

w. believes that there will be a literal 1000 year reign on earth

x. believes in prophecy

y. allow women to read scripture, pass communion, have title of "minister"

z. Makes examples and inferences a test of fellowship?

aa. Refuses to forgive those who have sinned against them.

bb.   Does not love their enemy.

cc.   Refuses to use their wealth to help those in need.

dd.   Will not forgive themselves for past sins.

ee.   Refuses to confess sins or admit to wrongs.

ff.   Believes and teaches baptismal regeneration.

gg.   Judges worldly people, but refuses to judge those who Claim to be Christians.

What did Jesus mean when he said to the Jews, "the kingdom will be taken away from you, and given to those who will bear its fruit?"

Romans 14: Kingdom Matters and Disputable Matters

In Disputable Matters – Liberty, In Matters Where God has given a Command – Unity, and in all Matters – Love!

**Kingdom matters=clear requirement/command of God one way or the other.

**Disputable matters are matters where many Christians have strong convictions. but where God has given no command and has no clear requirement.

Instructions: Mark the following matters either Disputable (D) Or Kingdom Matters (K) according to your present understanding:

___building church buildings

___having a special table for the Lord's supper

___Only certain men passing communion

___Drinking wine without getting drunk

___Dancing without lusting

___Repentance of sins

___Instrumental hymns at home

___Having a located preacher

___bread before cup in the Lord's Supper

___Wearing a tie to serve

___Confessing Jesus as Lord

___the practice of "leading" a prayer

___praying in secret

___everyone praying out loud together

___passing contribution trays

___giving in secret

___Remembering Jesus as often as you partake of the Lord's Supper

___Taking the Lord's Supper "on the night he was betrayed"(Th)

___Making melody in your heart

___using drums or tapping your feet

___being filled with the Holy Spirit

___meeting for worship in homes

___ wearing knee pants to worship

___wearing overalls to worship

___wearing fancy clothes and fancy hairstyles

___Observing Christmas and Easter as Religious Holy Days

____ Eating meat sacrificed to Idols
____Baptism in water to receive the Holy Spirit
____circumcision of boys
____must teach the lost to be saved yourself
____song books, microphones, overhead machines, and videos
____having musical notes
____having announcements
____women as Sunday School teachers
____Having Sunday School
____must have more than one elder
____must have more than one deacon
____Men must have short hair
____Women must have long hair
____Having only One congregation per city
____Men raise hands in prayer
____Christians should fast
____must give 10% of income or "exceed the scribes and Pharisees"
____clapping at home or at ball games
____clapping at baptisms
____eating meat with blood in it
____ Church Membership

Now that you've finished. answer the following questions:
1. What process or rule did you use to determine which issues were disputable and which were kingdom issues?
2. Can you worship and work with those who marked their lists differently than you?
3. Which issues are absolutely essential and must be done right for one to be saved?
4. Can you fellowship with those who disagree with you?
5. How sure are you of your answers: 100 % sure, 90% 80%, 50%, 20%, ...not sure at all
6. What does God think of people who are divisive regarding Matters that are disputable?
7. How would the Devil like to use "disputable matters?"

152

Anonymous Question

(The real heart- felt questions that our postmodern plus young people do not feel safe asking parents, teachers, or church leaders)

1. What does the Church of Christ have that is better than other churches?
2. Why do the rules at Harding suddenly change for you once you're married?
3. Can your sex life be too obscene in the eyes of God? (I'm into a lot of weird things)
4. How do you forgive someone for hurting your wife, husband or children?
5. How young is too young to get married?
6. Does God really decide our salvation or our life in advance?
7. Is premarital sex really condemned in the Bible?
8. What is lust? Just thinking about sex with the other person? Can you sin by lusting if you're not married and therefore would not be committing adultery?
9. How can a man and wife teach their children problem resolution if they do not argue in front of their kids?
10. Can a woman baptize someone they led to Christ?
11. How do you deal with doubt about your spouse – if they are being honest?
12. If you have been abused do you have to tell your spouse?
13. How do you make your wife not feel used sexually?
14. How do we, as couples, become more spiritual?
15. Do you divorce if your spouse has an affair?
16. How do your keep your kids spiritual through teenage years?
17. How do you know if the person you are with is someone you could live w/ forever?
18. How can you stop fearing about divorce?
19. How can I learn to trust when it's my problem and not my boyfriend's?
20. How can I get closer to God?
21. How can I make God my first love?
22. Denominations – I believe the concept of different denominations goes against the spirit of Christianity…when did this begin?
23. How do my wife and I work through my premarital sex life? She never even dated   anyone before me, but I was involved sexually as a teenager.
24. What are ways to get over a difference of opinion without getting into a fight?
25. How should you approach your children about sex?
26. How much money is "enough"?
27. Why is it so hard to forgive?
28. What is "unequally yoked"?
29. What color is my mansion in heaven?
30. Is "Christian Rock" right or wrong?
31. How do you forget a hurtful thing that was said/done early in the relationship?
32. How do I keep from blurting hurtful things during a fight?
33. How do I keep from being tempter when approached with an offer for sex, it's easy to say no, but thinking no is harder?
34. What id you want to stay home with your kids – but it is not financially possible?
35. What is the purpose of going through a marriage ceremony? Are there any examples in
36. The Bible? Why can't a couple just mutually be together and "decide" to be "husband and wife"? What is marriage?
37. If God knows your heart, then is there a point in a couples' relationship that God sees them as married even if they are not "legally married"?
38. How do you improve your love life when sex is uncomfortable to you?
39. How can I best lead my family as a man?
40. What can I do to protect my family from Satan?
41. If God is no respecter of person, then why would He make exceptions?
42. How do I accept defeat (fights, and sin)?
43. Usually, I want sex very often. What do I do when I want sex and my wife doesn't?
44. How do you deal with little annoyance? I.e. Chewing, slurping, etc.

153

45. How do I tell my mom that I am ok and doing fine without her questioning my wife?
46. If you have an important decision in life or in marriage, how will you know where God is leading you?
47. How can a man encourage modesty among women or confront an immodest woman?
48. What physical contact is appropriate in a dating relationship?
49. How can Christians justify Spring Sing (or anything) if they are opposed to it being too spiritual?
50. What is natural family planning?
51. How does a man control his sexual urges after a lost spouse (death)?
52. From my understanding, a man and a woman become husband and wife at their wedding
53. When the preacher announces them as husband and wife. However, I have heard
54. Some people say to truly become one after their wedding they must have sex to consummate their marriage. What do you think?
55. What about birth control? Is it wrong of ok in God's eyes?
56. The Church of Christ believes if you are not a member of that faith you will not go to heaven, but God denies no one so why do they believe that?
57. Why doesn't the Church of Christ believe in the use of instruments when Psalms
58. Repeatedly instructs us to worship God with the harp of cymbals or etc…(instruments)?
59. Why don't people ever talk about the blessedness of single life, and how much a person can use their youth for Christ instead of living for marriage and "dating"?
60. If we look like God, does he look feminine too? Or more masculine?
61. Can someone be ready to be married in 6 months, but know the person they are marrying for 4 months?
62. How can someone do communion and pray in church but get drunk on church trips and get away with but God knowing?
63. What does Satan look like?
64. How can you find the will of God?
65. How do you balance the role of women in a job while she's single and the role of married women in the church?
66. Should I date or do courtship?
67. How do you witness to relatives who profess Christ but live differently?
68. Should my brother go on depression meds if the real problem is both spiritual and mental?
69. How can I tell if the guy I like is <u>really</u> spiritual?
70. How does one conquer obsessive/bothersome thought?
71. Why do you thing that God made sex before marriage a sin?
72. Does having doubt about your Christianity mean that you are not saved or is it merely another tool used by the Devil to distract?
73. If a church of Christ member believes it is wrong to worship with music, shouldn't they believe that all music is wrong?
74. As a church of Christ member, every other member I have seen has had the opinion that music is not bad as long as it doesn't leave negative ????? Isn't it better to listen to Christian music with instruments than non-Christian music? Why is it considered a sin then?
75. If you want something really bad and you think about it and it's wrong then is it really that ???? to do it?
76. Is masturbation wrong? And why?
77. Is it true that Christ had brothers and sister or are "the brothers" of Jesus any person?
78. How do you know if God wants you to be with someone?
79. Is it true that God will lead you to the right person or are you the one who picks your husband/wife?
80. How come women must be obedient to their husband?
81. Is God a pro-macho being?
82. Was Joseph, Mary's husband, a saint?
83. Some churches believe in saints living among us, do they exist?
84. How do you know what church is the real church of God?
85. Does sin have different weights?
86. Is there a purgatory/place in between?
87. Where do I begin in strengthening my spiritual life?

88. How do we as humans not only forgive, but forget another's trespass? Especially when the other person does not ask for forgiveness?
89. How do you know that your prayers are sincere and not merely routine?
90. If you are a member of the church and the elders and deacons can't decide on a preacher or have other issues causing a split, who is in the right or wrong? Where's the middle ground?
91. Does an elder have to stop being an elder when he loses his spouse?
92. Is it easy to get an "A" in here?
93. Where do dinosaurs come from?
94. What is heavy petting?
95. There are always people who are not saved but will be someday. Since God knows all, if he came back and those people didn't get saved, what happens?
96. What if you don't want to, but continue to do the same sin, are you forgiven if you are really sorry, but fall time and again?
97. Is there unforgivable sin?
98. The bible talks about Christian dating and being unevenly yoked is not allowed. How can you really know this and is it wrong to date someone who is more or less spiritual than you?
99. How do you know that "the one" you think is "the one" really is "the one"?
100. Do we each have a personal guardian angel?
101. language and slang change dramatically from each generation to the next, so how can we expect to take what was written thousands of years ago literally?
102. Will society always revolve around sex?
103. Is alcohol okay as long as it isn't taken in large amounts as to affect our behavior?
104. Will homosexuality become accepted as a trait rather than a sin?
105. Interracial marriage is ok, right?
106. What does God say about dating?
107. What does God say about who to choose for a mate?
108. How to deal with drugs and alcohol? What does God say about how to deal with it?
109. What does the bible say about drugs and drinking?
110. What does the Bible say about tattoos and body piercing? What if the tattoos exalt God?
111. People always tell me to "listen to God" but how do I know when he is speaking to me and what is he saying?
112. Is it really wrong to drink if you don't get drunk?
113. When someone dies people say that God thinks it's their time. Does Satan have any powers associated with death and could it really be his time to take a loved one from you?
114. What does the NT say about inter-racial marriages?
115. How do you forgive yourself if a friend dies without you ever telling them about Jesus?
116. The Bible says that divorce is wrong unless for reasons of marital unfaithfulness-
117. What if one spouse is being beaten by the other? Is divorce still wrong?
118. If you don't believe that baptism is necessary, yet you still are baptized, how does God view that?
119. Is masturbation a sin?
120. How long was a day for God when he created the earth?
121. Is there a mister/misses right for everyone?
122. Is God real?
123. Is it true that you marry your best friend whether you think it won't work out?
124. Why do guys think you shouldn't tell the truth, even though it says not to lie in the Bible?
125. Is it really wrong to divorce if your marriage goes down the drain?
126. Can you change someone who is doing wrong, but want to change?
127. I asked for forgiveness over and over but I never changed. Why?
128. Are you considered a sinner b/c you listen to rap music?
129. What is the best way to approach a friend who is lost without scaring them off?
130. Are there certain degrees of rewards in heaven or is everyone equally rewarded?
131. How does God go about giving salvation to OT people?
132. Explain your views on varying churches believing they are the only true church.
133. Give your views on Mormonism.

155

134. I have a friend whose aunt had been divorced due to abuse…she was then not allowed to join a church of Christ congregation. How does that possibly support God's way of giving everyone the opportunity to come to him? I was shocked when they told me about it.
135. I'm in a serious relationship…how am I sure he's THE ONE?
136. What happened to Jimmy Hoffa?
137. When do you know you found the right one?
138. Why do bad things happen to good people?
139. How do you know when a girl/guy is flirting with you?
140. Is there more than one type of love?
141. Should you kiss on the first date?
142. What happens if you don't have a strong prayer life?
143. Does everyone have an angel?
144. Who did Adam and eve's children have sex with?
145. What does it mean to be righteous?
146. I'm not saying baptism isn't necessary, but when is someone actually saved? (the moment he/she accepts God into their heart or the moment after they have been dunked?) is it possible for us not to sin?
147. Some people say the when you meet your future mate, you will "know" is that always the case? Or do some relationships take time?
148. What do you suggest to help a Christian keep a good Christian walk daily?
149. How can you help strengthen fiends who are weak in their faith without appearing like you are better than them?
150. Why don't we sing black gospel?
151. How do you learn to forgive?
152. Is it wrong to smoke or drink?
153. If you're gay will you be forgiven? (I'm not gay, just asking)
154. Is it wrong to cuss?
155. How far can you go on a date?
156. Why aren't there any temples today and what about a living prophet?
157. In taking the Lord's supper, do we <u>have</u> to use unleavened bread and grape juice?
158. Isn't it just symbolic anyways? Could we use bread and H2O?
159. How can you break a hard heart that God has asked you to break?
160. My roommate is very homesick and cries all of the time, how can I comfort her and make her feel better?
161. Is it wrong to listen to worship songs on the radio with instruments our of "worship service"?
162. Is dating necessary to find your husband or is it better to be friends?
163. If you send your children when they are young to Christian schools to keep them from the environment, who ministers to the public schools?
164. How do you know when you really love someone?
165. Is it wrong to marry outside your religion?
166. Is it wrong to drink alcoholic beverages once of the legal age?
167. How can catholics think they're right?
168. What and how much can Christians drink when it comes to alcohol?
169. What did you want to be when you were small?
170. How do you get sinful thoughts out of your head?
171. What are my limits in God's service as a woman?
172. Do young children automatically go to heaven?
173. How many times can you be baptized?
174. How do you deal with people who have wronged you that you have to deal with?
175. Are catholics rooted in Voodoo in Latin countries?
176. What if you marry the wrong person?
177. What do you do if your spouse has raped someone in the past?
178. How do I go about discussing what I think about baptism when I don't even know if I think it is essential or not?
179. Is it possible today that people can still use gifts such as prophecy, tongues (speaking in), etc?

156

180. Does God lead the right person to me for marriage and then I decide if I want to marry them or do I have to pick by myself?

181. When men lust after women in their minds but do not act on these thought, is this sin between God, the man and the woman, or just between the man and God?

182. It says in Matthew 5 that the only reason to justify divorce was adultery, but what about abuse? Is abuse of the spouse and/or children biblically justified?

183. I was reading in Corinthians I think, it was talking about speaking in tongues, So, why doesn't the COC do it?

184. Can you be baptized again if you feel that you've screwed up more than you think you can handle forgiving yourself?

185. Does it matter what music I listen to?

186. Is smoking anything substance abuse?

187. If I work on Sunday will I go to hell?

188. How do you convince someone about when you are really saved (through baptism) when they only believe with their heart?

189. How do you argue against drinking w/ someone who is not a Christian?

190. Is it wrong to watch "R" rated movies if you don't let them influence you?
how can I tell God has picked someone for me?

191. How will I know it's him or her?

192. How can parents teach their young children the bible?

193. How does bad luck go w/ prayers/ how do you become over hurt that your spouse has caused?

194. What does is take to get close to God?

195. How do you make someone you love understand God's will is not to live in sin?

196. Why does harding insist on having curfew all 4 years? And live on campus?

197. Why does Harding make the rules so drastic and always threaten to "fine" us or kick us out? Doesn't seem very Godly to me, personally.

198. Are we going to know each other in heaven?

199. Are you happy here?

200. Why do church of Christ people doesn't believe in the Holly Spirit?

201. How do I know that that someone that God has for me is exactly what I want?

202. What do you do if you like someone that is not a Christian?

203. Is it wrong to marry someone who doesn't go to church?

204. Is it wrong to clap hands in services and during songs since clapping is simulating musical instruments and it has no meaning?

205. Is there one person made for us to marry?

206. If your husband beats you can you be scripturally divorced?

207. How did the early church know which books to put in the Bible?

208. Why do some scriptures show up in some early manuscripts and not others? Does this jeopardize their authority?

209. Where are the scriptures that are used to support non-instrumental singing?

210. The Bible says "not a hint of sexual immorality" is it really immoral if you love the person?

211. My dad cheated on my mom this year but they stayed together. I know this will affect my future relationships. How do I get past that?

212. Is it that bad to drink occasionally? I mean, does it say in the Bible to not drink?

213. I work with some gay guys. I think that they can't help the feelings but they can help the action. What do you think?

214. Is it bad to be scared of eternity?

215. Is it a sin to want to experience life here on earth before going to heaven?

216. What is good scriptures to start with when starting a bible study?

217. How do you study with people from different religions, especially ones with there own bible (Book).

218. Is it bad to drink alcohol, even if you don't get drunk?

219. How come women don't know what they or can't make up their mind?

220. How do you get rid of guilt?

221. How do you tell whose right for you?

222. How do you deal w/ people who are Christians but don't have Christian morals or standards?

157

223. How do you open up to someone after being hurt badly by someone else?
224. Why don't we as Christians come together rather than be separated by a name? It seems that if this were the first century and we being persecuted, we wouldn't be worrying about denominational differences.
225. Are people who are baptized but don't believe it is necessary saved?
226. I have grown up in a Christian home, but been allowed to dance. I am social and enjoy being involved @ school functions, but I have seen many things that aren't pure. Now that I think about having children I don't want to hold them back socially, because I understand but should I let them be in the position?
227. Is using tobacco wrong?
228. Is clapping in worship wrong?
229. Is church mandatory or is it alright to worship at home with your family and friends?
230. Are instruments in worship wrong?
231. When is Jesus coming back?
232. Is it a sin to skip church or for elders to change service times for a big event?
233. How much can you drink before it's a sin?
234. Are tattoos and piercings wrong?
235. Since the act of baptism doesn't give you remission of sins, is it mandatory?
236. Should prayer be mental or verbal?
237. How do we know our career will serve God? What happens when it takes a different path?
238. If Harding is committed to being Christ-like, does not the process of "initiation" of social clubs contradict that philosophy?
239. I study and pray but still don't feel close to God. Am I trying too hard? How can I get over that?
240. How do I deal with my gay friends?
241. How can I talk to my family about God?
242. Why does it say in I Corinthians 11:2-16 that women cover their heads in worship but we do not obey this today? Was this only relevant to the Corinthians or should we still be obeying this scripture today?
243. What if you love your spouse and were brought together through church, but feel that maybe this is not who God intended for you to marry?

244. I don't know how to change my attitude towards my parents to be a light to them.
245. I have many hard feelings towards my in-laws and I don't know how to overcome them.
246. How far is too far?
247. Do children who die go to heaven?
248. What characteristics should I look for in a mate/
249. Why do boys and girls think differently?
250. Should you tell about your past to a boyfriend/girlfriend?
251. In a relationship, what "red flags" should you be more cautious of?
252. Ex: if he doesn't think a drink is wrong or smoking is wrong, would that be something to avoid if I disagree with him?
253. What are a couple of key things to make sure of when dating or marrying someone?
254. What is sexually active? Only having sex or other things?
255. How do you tell if you don't love your spouse?
256. Do you think God likes birth control?
257. Has God already planed how many children we should have and we're trying to control it?
258. What if you don't enjoy having sex with your husband?
259. How many times will God forgive the same sin?
260. During worship of any kind is it ok to worship God with people that clap their hands when you don't believe in clapping?
261. Is going to the beach ok when there are people there with not much on?
262. If Christians know that homosexuality is wrong, then why is there a lot of homosexuals in the Church of Christ and Harding?

158

263. Is it fair for a previously very sexually active person to want to marry a virgin?
264. Why do girls want to have to many children?
265. Do they not realize a mother and father can't spend a lot of time with many children?
266. The Bible says that a woman is saved through childbearing, What if you're a woman that doesn't want to even get married, let alone have a kid?
267. How do I show my younger sister the right path to dating, when I wasn't shown by my older sisters?
268. How can I know the difference between someone I want to date and someone God wants me to date?
269. How far is too far before marriage?
270. If drugs were legal, like marijuana, since they are grown naturally, would it be ok to use but not abuse?
271. What are ways to forgive yourself for things you have done, even after you've asked for God's already?
272. How can I not blame God for taking a loved one away at a young age?
273. What can a son or daughter do when the parents are fighting?
274. Why does Harding boast of being a Christian school when everyone is so fake?
275. Should you always be completely honest with your spouse?
276. What if I am not attracted to my spouse?
277. Will I know my spouse in Heaven or is death really final for the relationship?
278. What if a married couple does not enjoy sex?
279. Is there someone out there for everyone? I'm scared I'll never find anyone.)
280. If I have already had sex can there still be a good Christian man who can love me?
281. If I have been pregnant, but miscarried should I tell the boy who was going to be the father?
282. How can I stop being sexual active?
283. How can my friend tell her husband that their baby is not his?
284. If you have had sex already, do you need to tell your future spouse what you have done?
285. Is masturbation wrong?
286. If I'm not a virgin anymore, should I marry a virgin or just not care anymore?
287. If I have been sexually active in the past, and now am starting a relationship with a good Christian virgin, when should I share my past, how should I and how much should I reveal?
288. What do you say to a friend who is struggling with their faith, or a death of someone close, or an eating disorder?
289. Is instrumental music wrong in the worship? IN my car? Etc.
290. What advice could I give to a friend who is seriously considering marrying a person who is a Christian but not of the same religion. They do not agree on major things such as baptism and the Lord's Supper.
291. How can I tactfully approach a family member who is living in sin without driving him or her farther from Christ?
292. Are there any limits on what sexual acts are acceptable within marriage?
293. Can angels get inside people just like demons to do work?
294. Is masturbation a sin?
295. Are there any unforgiven sin?
296. Do you believe in angels?
297. Why is there racism in the church?
298. What to do if I find out my Christian friend is a homosexual?
299. Why do I feel as if I cannot find a Christian woman?
300. Should I be more concerned with living my Christian life or trying to go to heaven?
301. How can I get excited about anything, including God?
302. Do you believe that remarriage is ok?
303. How will affect the kids?

159

304. There is so much talk about God and miracles and guardian angels. Well, if there are guardian angels where was the person I care for's guardian angel and why didn't God perform a miracle so she could live. He used to do miracles in the bible, but why not now?

305. How do you build up trust with someone, if you have been hurt in a past relationship?

306. If you are dating someone why you really care about and they have a bad past with dealing with drugs and sex-how do you truly get past that and accept that they have changed?

307. What part in a Christian's relationship with the other sex does physical attraction have?

308. What if you're not sure you were baptized for the right reasons?

309. Is it possible that God would allow you to marry the "wrong" person?

310. How can you tell when it's time to get married?

311. How far is to far before you are married?

312. How do you deal with a parent who always seems to bring down the child, never opening up or being a true parent to them. Especially when they wouldn't listen to anyone when confronted about the selfish attitude?

313. Is masturbation wrong?

314. How do you be the man in a dating relationship?

315. Is masturbation alright to do?

316. How far is too far on a date?

317. What denominations are going to heaven?

318. Is it ok to have friends who smoke, do drugs, swear, drink, or are gay?

319. How do you love someone you hate?

320. Why did the enrollment go up and they didn't make any more parking spots?

321. Why is cursing considered wrong? (they're just words)

322. Why don't I love my girlfriend like I use to

323. I'm engaged and I have some doubts, how do I know if it's right?

324. Is oral sex wrong with your spouse?

325. If God knows all that is an every has been, then he knew from the start on who will be saved and who won't. How can this be?

326. What do you believe is the main component for marriage, other than a spiritual bond?

327. How do I know when the man is being genuine and true with me?

328. Is there really someone out there for me?

329. Is it right in God's eyes for a Christian to remarry after divorce, or is it adultery?

330. If I'm a Christian and have strong morals, why am I attracted to "bad guys" and not Christian ones?

331. Is it limiting God by saying I only want to marry another virgin?

332. Is oral sex inside marriage wrong?

333. When and how much dancing is ok?

334. How can we raise Christian children in a secular world?

335. How can I be an example for Christ in the business world?

336. How do I reach our to a friend who has fallen away from Christ?

337. What should I tell my kids about what I've done in the past?

338. Should I completely forget about what God has previously forgiven me for?

339. What do you do if you feel like you do so much for your wife but its seems it is never enough?

340. Is it safe to get married while you're young?

341. Why do men leave their families (mid-life crisis)?

342. Is taking nap with your boyfriend wrong?

343. Do you forgive a spouse for adultery even when they are still cheating?

344. Is messing around wrong?

345. How do you know if who you are with is the one?

346. When do you know if you really like someone again or if it is just a really good friendship?

347. Should you reveal stuff about your past if the person doesn't ask?

348. How do you answer the question "why didn't God let me keep my baby?" and how do you convince your wife that God works through stillborn children?

349. How far is too far on a date?

160

350. If the bible is inspired, and all of it true, yet Daniel and Revelations are Apocraphical, this not to be taken literally, is the entire bible true? Does that mean there are several ways to salvation, or does baptism=the only way, or one way

351. What is the best way to combat jealousy in a relationship?

352. What is the average size of the male penis?

353. If you are in a relationship – why do couples have so many problems? Is it a sign that you shouldn't be together?

354. Is looking at porn (magazines, shows, etc) adultery

355. How does sexual abuse effect a marriage (even after counseling)

356. Why aren't guys more considerate

357. I want to find a guy just like my dad and I compare everyone to him-is that ok?

358. My parents are very open a/b intimacy and are very affectionate toward each other in public and I want to be affectionate too in public-is that ok?

359. Do demons exist in physical form?

360. How do you know when it's the right person to marry?

361. If you have problems in a relationship but always get through them, is that meant to be?

362. What's the difference in drugs and prescription drugs? Such as prescription marijuana and not prescription?

363. How do you overcome the feeling of second place within my marriage. (Ex-boyfriend died, she cried for two weeks, a night and whenever I am around, I feel pushed aside)

364. What should you do if you were sexually active but then was saved-my old girlfriend won't let go --what do I do?

365. How many times have you slept on the couch?

366. Is it ok to work somewhere they serve alcohol?

367. How do you broach the subject of what you want in a spouse with a date?

368. Is it wrong not to date other people while you are waiting for that special person to come along?

369. Is it wrong not to want to stay at home with my children? Can I work when they enter school?

370. When is the exact point I experience Jesus when I do? How do I say "that's how I've seen Jesus in my life."?

371. Was I too young at ten to become a Christian? I never had doubts until last semesters Psych. Class we talk about the age of accountability. How much exactly do I have to know?

372. How can I better fight doubt and still serve God actively?

373. How do you cheer up a roommate who just wants to have a boyfriend just like everyone else in her suite?

374. Do you trust your friends when they tell you, you should not be dating the person you are?

375. I have read that if someone leaves the church and rejects Jesus as his Lord – and later decides to repent he must be re-baptized. Should he?

376. How do you know when you are ready for marriage?

377. Can you be 100% sure you have found "the one"? Is there "the one"?

378. Is there a easy or better way to tell your parents you are engaged if they think you are too young?

379. Where do we draw the line between focusing on what is good, commendable, and beautiful and focusing on what is not where movies and music are concerned? Can I not watch a movie or listen to music and appreciate the God given talents and give him praise for those even though bad language and sex may be contained? It seems to me that those who cannot are focusing on the bad things and not the good ones.

380. Generally speaking, do guys? Or girls? Forgive past sexual misconduct easier?

381. What is the extent of alcohol consumption that is "right" with God?

382. Is it wrong to drink anything even at a minor level?

383. What should you do if you suspect a friend has an eating disorder?

384. How did you choose your career?

385. What are your feelings on birth control? What biblical basis do you have for this?

386. If you're dating someone who has a lot of the qualities you're looking for in a mate, but not all, then should you move on and look for someone who does?

387. How do you draw the line between a "comfortable" life and being materialistic?

161

I Refuse to Quit
(A Tribute to Christian Teachers)

I am a foot soldier of the Lord and I serve on the battleground for the hearts and minds of young people. I have been washed In the blood of the Lamb, and filled with His Spirit----I serve in the power of Almighty God. I am His slave by choice. My name is in the book~ I will serve Him with every last breath. I will not back down!

I will not stop when Satan attacks! This is War! My armor is buckled, for I know where I stand-- I am an enemy of the Deceiver! I know who paid the price for me. I will not exchange this battle ground for the fame of the spotlight or for larger paychecks in the world! I submit myself to the criticism of the world and its values. I am finished with shallow earthly goals, and giving my energy for short term pleasures. I'm locked on the target. My aim will not waver. I will dream big for I serve the God who made the world.

I choose to die in the battle for children! Criticism of earthbound parents and students will not shake my vision. I don't need awards, honors, or promotions to push me forward. My Mansion is being built. My treasures are stored up for me. The Man on the cross is all the motivation I'll ever need.

I know I'll see struggle, and perspiration, but I am driven by inspiration! I will not be lured away, bought, or shamed into leaving. Parents may blame me, and students may malign me--but I will not be distracted from my goal. I will not sell out to shallow earthly trinkets. I will not back down from personal sacrifice, and I will not shut up when my message is called old fashioned. When the public mocks me as narrow minded and bigoted, I will not stop working---because I have a vision of one with wounded hands and feet---and He loves children!